PLACE DU LOU
PLACE DU PALAIS ROIAL
Roial
QUINZE VINGTS
Richelieu
R. des Frondeurs
Rue d'Argenteuil
Honoré
S. ROCH
Roch
des Moulins

DIDEROT'S LETTERS TO SOPHIE VOLLAND

£1.50

Diderot in 1760 from
Chenu's engraving of the
portrait by Garand (see p. 59)

# Diderot's Letters to Sophie Volland

A selection translated by

Peter France

*London*

OXFORD UNIVERSITY PRESS

1972

*Oxford University Press, Ely House, London W. 1*

GLASGOW NEW YORK TORONTO MELBOURNE WELLINGTON
CAPE TOWN SALISBURY IBADAN NAIROBI DAR ES SALAAM LUSAKA ADDIS ABABA
BOMBAY CALCUTTA MADRAS KARACHI LAHORE DACCA
KUALA LUMPUR SINGAPORE HONG KONG TOKYO

ISBN 0 19 212551 6



Printed in Great Britain
by W & J Mackay Limited, Chatham

# CONTENTS

# INTRODUCTION

Horace Walpole, visiting Paris in 1765, thought Diderot 'a very lively old man, and great talker'. The 'old' is faintly shocking to readers of Diderot, but the 'great talker' is right. His friends put it more enthusiastically. In their eyes he was the inspired prophet, the genius of conversation. 'When he began to talk and let his rich store of thoughts flow freely, forgetting his theories [of artistic composition] and abandoning himself to the impulse of the moment, then indeed he was irresistible', writes Marmontel in his memoirs. The drawback was that Diderot was unable to concentrate on literary production—or so Marmontel said: 'In his writing, he never succeeded in constructing a unified whole; that initial process of arranging everything and putting it in its proper place was too slow and too tedious for him. He wrote by inspiration, before thinking anything out; the result is that he wrote some fine pages, as he said himself, but he never composed a book.' (Diderot, as if in reply, said of Marmontel: 'He doesn't know the meaning of conversation.') Marmontel is not quite fair; Diderot was not incapable of organization—we have only to think of his triumphant editing of the *Encyclopédie* (seventeen volumes of text and almost as many of plates) over a period of twenty-five years. It is true, however, that he never set himself to the great task of writing a master work like Montesquieu's *De l'esprit des lois* or Rousseau's *Émile*. He let himself be distracted, even exploited, by friends and by strangers; he poured out his wealth in letters to friends, impromptu diatribes, and ephemeral journalism rather than channelling his energies into the creation of great treatises, epics, or even novels.

So much the better, we may say. Between the monumental genres and the impermanence of talk lies the middle region of the journal, the dialogue, the anti-novel, the commentary, the thought, reflexion or maxim, the essay and the letter. This is Diderot's territory; here we can situate those works which make him so close to us, *Le Neveu de Rameau, Jacques le Fataliste*, the *Salons*, the philosophical dialogues. And with these we must place the letters to Sophie Volland, 'resplendent', in the words of Henri Lefebvre, 'beyond all literature and writing, with the directness of the spoken word, the luminous warmth of communication, the living presence of a man.'

None of these masterpieces was printed in Diderot's lifetime. The man who believed so fervently in posterity either did not dare or did not care to bolster up his reputation by publication. In 1765, he is gratified, as he says to Sophie in letter 30, that 'my vanity can do without popular applause'. To write for an audience of one or two (Sophie and Grimm) is enough for him. Another time, after criticizing a recently published historical work of Voltaire, he says to Sophie: 'I would rather have written this letter to my love. It will be buried between us. She will enjoy reading it as I have enjoyed writing it and this is all that is needed.'

For the letters to Sophie are love letters. Unlike many correspondences of the time, they were not intended as semi-public gazettes to be read aloud to news-hungry circles in the provinces. Sophie might read selected passages to her sisters or her mother; otherwise Diderot was quite content that they should never see the light. They were written rapidly, spontaneously, apparently without any sort of rough draft. Once written, they were forgotten; Diderot took no copies and often could not remember what he had written the week before. So these letters are often eloquent, but never studied. In them we catch something of the natural vigour, variety, and irresistible flow of their author's conversation—not a book, but a man speaking to a woman.

They have become a book for all that. Of the 500 or more letters sent by Diderot to Sophie 189 are left—a sizeable volume. We can regret the loss of the others, but what we have leads us straight to the heart of Diderot's existence in the most productive years of his life. The reader who knows Diderot's major writings will constantly be struck by the way in which these letters express the dominant ideas and feelings of the other works. The letters written in 1760 and 1761, for instance, give us the variations on vice and virtue and even some of the anecdotes and characters of *Le Neveu de Rameau*. In one sense this is Diderot's workshop. But it is much more than this; in the words of Diderot's biographer Arthur Wilson, these letters are 'unexcelled in their revelation both of a particularly interesting social milieu and of an infinitely rich, complex and humane personality.' Diderot himself, taking stock as Montaigne had done before him, says: 'My letters are a more or less faithful history of my life. Without meaning to, I am doing what I have so often wished for. Why, I said, an astronomer will spend thirty years of his life on top of an observatory, his eyes glued day and night to the end of a telescope, simply to determine the movement of a star, and no one makes a study of himself, no one has the courage to keep an accurate record of all the thoughts that come into his mind, all the feelings that agitate his heart, all his sorrows and joys.' The self-presentation is less deliberate and artful than Montaigne's, for Montaigne was writing a book, but the result is just as fascinating. We come to know Diderot in love and at work, we see him at home, in Paris, in the provinces and eventually on the road to Saint Petersburg, we are shown the comfortable life of the radical *philosophes*, the making of the *Encyclopédie*, and round this small world the larger world of art, literature, politics, religious controversy, war and peace. In the following pages I shall try to sketch some of the different milieux which overlap in Diderot's letters and to introduce some of the more important *dramatis personae*.

* * *

Let us start in Langres, an old town 150 miles south-east of Paris where Denis Diderot was born in 1713, the son of a respectable cutler (Didier). His father died in 1759, just after the first letter in this collection, but the son continued to be haunted by his memory, seeing in him the embodiment of the social virtues, justice, honesty, charity, paternal love. The philosopher emancipated himself from the life of the provincial bourgeoisie, but remained faithful to many of their moral values. Apart from Denis, two children survived the father, 'little sister' and 'the Abbé'. 'Little sister' was Denise, born in 1715, and described in a letter as 'lively, active, cheerful, resolute, quick to take offence, slow to forgive, without a care for the present or the future, free in her actions and even freer in her words, a sort of female Diogenes.' Diderot's younger brother 'the Abbé', his junior by eight years, was quite different; he seemed to Denis to embody all the bad effects of religious belief: 'The Abbé was born sensitive and serene. He would have been an intelligent man, but religion has filled him with scruples and fears. He is gloomy, taciturn, circumspect and disagreeable. He constantly carries around with him a measuring rod for judging his own behaviour and that of his fellows.' In 1759, in a visit to Langres which is recorded in these letters, Diderot settled the family affairs with his brother and sister; thereafter he received a small regular income from his home town, but rarely returned there. He remained on good terms with 'little sister', but not with the Abbé.

Diderot had been living in Paris ever since he had gone there as a young student. For many years he seems to have led a bohemian life, living ingloriously by the pen. In 1743, at about the time when he was beginning to make a name for himself, he married a poor girl, Anne-Antoinette Champion, against his father's wishes (indeed his father's immediate reaction was to shut his son up in a monastery). It was not to be a happy marriage. Perhaps Madame Diderot has not had a fair deal and certainly her husband was to blame for much of her bitterness, but the dismal impression we receive of her in these letters is borne out by Jean-Jacques Rousseau's description of her in his *Confessions* as 'a shrew and a fishwife'. By the time we meet them the couple are living and quarrelling in the Rue Taranne, close to Saint-Germain-des-Prés; of several children the only survivor is Angélique, born in 1753, the apple of her father's eye. Diderot took a great interest in his daughter's education and felt obliged to provide a handsome dowry for her. She later became a very talented performer on the harpsichord and married a young man from Langres, Caroillon de Vandeul. It was Vandeul and his wife who were largely responsible for the preservation and copying of Diderot's manuscripts.

Concern for his daughter and vestigial loyalty to his wife kept Diderot attached to the family home, but it was not the true centre of his life. The greater part of his time was spent with writers, artists, publishers, and *philosophes*; by *philosophes* is meant not philosophers in the present-day sense of the word, but intellectuals (often amateur scientists) who aligned themselves with the progressive views of the *Encyclopédie*. This encyclopedia was Diderot's main activity and source of revenue until 1765. He had begun work as general editor around 1745; at first he had as joint-editor the distinguished mathematician d'Alembert, soon to become a member of the Academy of Science and the French Academy, but d'Alembert virtually abandoned the enterprise when it ran into persecution in 1759. Editing the *Encyclopédie* was a complete existence; it meant planning the whole great work, writing numerous articles on every kind of subject, visiting the workshops of craftsmen to learn their trades, cajoling friends and colleagues, rewriting their contributions, correcting proofs, negotiating with publishers (the chief of these, Le Breton, appears frequently in these letters), and all the time struggling against the forces, political, legal and religious, which threatened to destroy his work. The final volumes of text appeared in 1765, after the *Encyclopédie* had been outlawed by the law-courts and surreptitiously censored by Le Breton, but even then Diderot was not free of his great burden; the final volume of plates only appeared in 1772.

The *Encyclopédie* took so much of Diderot's time and energy that one is astonished how much else he was able to write. There is no need to list all his works here. He had begun with translations, scandalous tales, and philosophical writings; in the late 1750s he produced some influential pieces of dramatic theory and two plays, *Le Fils naturel* and *Le Père de famille* (the titles typify Diderot's concern for family life). In 1760 a practical joke and a real event led to the polemical novel *La Religieuse*. Some time round 1761 he began what many consider his greatest work, the dialogue *Le Neveu de Rameau*, which in characteristic manner he reworked over the following years. Throughout the period covered by these letters he wrote the *Salons*, accounts of the biennial art exhibitions at the Louvre. The late 1760s and early 1770s were a productive period, with a series of philosophical dialogues including *Le Rêve de d'Alembert*, an important commentary on Helvétius's treatise *De l'homme*, the novel (or anti-novel) *Jacques le Fataliste*, the *Paradoxe du comédien* and many other smaller pieces ranging from short stories to the *Éléments de Physiologie*.

The majority of these writings were not printed in Diderot's lifetime. If they were read at all, it was by the tiny group of royal and noble subscribers to the manuscript *Correspondance littéraire*, which was distributed twice a month by Diderot's closest friend, Melchior Grimm. Grimm was a German who had come to Paris in 1749 as companion to the younger son of a count; he had been on the friendliest of terms with Rousseau and Diderot, both of them ten years his senior, and had quickly created a comfortable position for himself as a cultural middleman, keeping his noble patrons intelligently informed about intellectual and artistic life in Paris. It will be seen from the letters to Sophie that Diderot had an exalted affection for Grimm and sacrificed his time and talent to keep his friend supplied with copy. Rousseau gives us a black version of Grimm in his *Confessions*; we can hardly take his word as gospel, but it does look as if Diderot saw more in his friend than was really there. Indeed, even he complains increasingly of Grimm's despotism and not long before his death accuses him of egoism and cynical flattery: 'your soul has shrunk in Petersburg and Potsdam and in the antechambers of the great.' Be that as it may, we have Grimm to thank—indirectly—for a good deal of Diderot's best writing, above all the *Salons*.

For Diderot, Grimm and Sophie were the ideal audience; the three of them made up an inner circle of superior souls. Outside this inner circle is a host of friends and companions in the philosophical struggle with whom his relations were less constant. At times he appears as the sociable man, always ready to talk, listen, eat, and drink; at others he presents himself as the solitary, a man not made for the constant intercourse of polite society. The group in which he usually feels most at ease is the circle of the Baron d'Holbach, particularly when he goes to stay at the Baron's country estate of Le Grandval, a few miles east of Paris. Here is a glimpse of an autumn evening in 1760, and Diderot waiting in vain for a letter from Sophie.

> We are kept indoors by continual rain. Madame d'Holbach is ruining her eyes embroidering; Madame d'Aine is digesting, stretched out on a bed of cushions. Father Hoop is sitting there with his eyes half shut, his head down between his shoulders and his hands glued to his knees, dreaming of the end of the world, I expect. The Baron is reading, wrapped up in a dressing-gown and half-hidden under a night-cap. I am walking up and down, mechanically. I go over to the window to look at the weather, see the torrents of rain and subside into despair.

Paul-Henri Thiry d'Holbach always referred to in these letters as 'the Baron', was a rich German, born in 1723, who had settled permanently in France and devoted his time to entertaining his *philosophe* friends, to natural science (he contributed many articles on metallurgy and mineralogy to the *Encyclopédie*), and to atheist and rationalist propaganda. He was hospitable, but difficult to live with, and combined in a manner characteristic of his time a profound pessimism about societies both past and present and a surprising faith in the perfectibility of the human race. Also at Le Grandval we meet the Baron's eccentric mother-in-law, Madame d'Aine, and her daughter, the flirtatious Baroness (d'Holbach had previously been married to her older sister). Then there are the guests; among the regulars one must mention a Scot nicknamed 'Father' Hoop, a witty cynic about whom nothing is known for certain apart from what Diderot tells us, Charles-Georges Le Roy, the philandering Lieutenant of the Park of Versailles who wrote several articles on rural subjects for the *Encyclopédie*, and the Neapolitan diplomat Abbé Galiani, famous for his stories, but subsequently the author of a much-admired pamphlet on the grain trade. Diderot confides to Sophie in a letter not included here: 'Abbé Galiani shocked me greatly by confessing that he had never wept in his life'—for him there was always a close bond between tears and virtue.

The Holbach clan, as Rousseau calls them, is the group we see most frequently in these letters, but Diderot was also a visitor at Madame d'Épinay's country houses, La Chevrette and La Briche. It was in the grounds of La Chevrette that Rousseau had found a refuge in the Hermitage and had written much of his greatest work. In 1757 he had broken spectacularly with Madame d'Épinay and the whole coterie of *philosophes*; his account of this is to be found in Book 9 of the *Confessions*. Madame d'Épinay, who was an intelligent woman and something of an intellectual, was Grimm's mistress; together they formed one of those quasi-official couples which were so common in the Paris of their day. A similar *ménage*, also embroiled with Rousseau, was that of Madame d'Épinay's cousin, Madame d'Houdetot, and her lover, the officer-poet Saint-Lambert. Occasionally the complaisant husbands appear on the scene, but it is the lovers who provide examples of affection and fidelity. The La Chevrette household was less radically 'philosophical' than that of the Baron; the two groups lived on good terms until 1762 when they were split by a complicated series of quarrels and intrigues. Diderot appears torn between them; occasionally he is driven to exclaim 'A plague on both your houses.'

In Paris we meet many of the same faces as at these country houses (the Baron receives his circle royally in the Rue Royale), but there are also various friends whose work keeps them in town. It is unnecessary to present most of these in this introduction, but I must at least say a word or two about Etienne-Noël Damilaville, who like Grimm and d'Holbach was ten years younger than Diderot. Damilaville was an invaluable man to the *philosophes*; his position in the Income Tax Office (*Bureau du Vingtième*) gave him the possibility of acting as a free mailbox for his friends—and these friends included Diderot and Voltaire. Diderot has a lot to say about his postal arrangements; the essential thing is that in order for his letters to travel free of charge from Paris to the provinces, they had to go with the official mail and be countersigned by Damilaville or his superiors, Gaudet or Courteilles. They then went to some official in the provinces (e.g. Gillet at Vitry-le-François) before being delivered to Sophie. Sophie's letters came back the same way and were usually delivered to Damilaville's office at the Quai des Miramionnes on the Ile Saint-Louis. In an obituary Grimm describes Damilaville as tedious and disagreeable, but Diderot seems to have liked his company and they spent many evenings together. Sometimes they were accompanied by Damilaville's mistress Madame Duclos, the wife of a colleague, who was eventually supplanted by Madame de Maux, a friend of Madame d'Épinay's, not long before Damilaville's painful death in 1768.

These are some of Diderot's closest friendships; around this narrow circle we catch frequent glimpses of the bigger world of the philosophers, scientists, writers, and artists of eighteenth-century Paris, the world of Buffon, Helvétius, Marmontel, Sedaine, Falconet, and Vanloo. Diderot is on good terms with many such people, but his position is outside the intellectual establishment; in spite of all Voltaire's persuasion, he refuses to become a candidate for the French Academy. Similarly, while he has many acquaintances with access to authority and himself has friendly professional dealings with Sartine, the lieutenant of police, he never walks the corridors of power. His force is in the book and his faith in posterity. After all, in 1749 he had been imprisoned as the disreputable free-thinking author of the *Lettre sur les aveugles*.

The network of *philosophes* extends far beyond Paris. Two Genevan names occur again and again throughout these letters, Rousseau, citizen of Geneva, and Voltaire, who had taken up residence just outside the city. Diderot had been a close friend of Jean-Jacques between 1742 and 1755; he had considered himself the Genevan's literary mentor and had conscripted him to write articles on music and political economy for the *Encyclopédie*. But in 1756 Rousseau had broken with the *philosophes* and had gone to live and write in the country; his relations with Diderot became strained and hostile until eventually in 1758 there was a mutual declaration of war. There was not to be any reconciliation; both men, who were in many ways so close, spoke bitterly of one another until the end of their lives. With Voltaire it was quite different. Where Rousseau and Diderot are the same age and resemble warring brothers, Voltaire and Diderot are allies in the same struggle while politely remote from each other. Voltaire is a man of the previous generation; Diderot admires him for his fight against intolerance, thinks highly of some of his writing, regrets his vanity and envious criticism, and does not allow himself to be cajoled and protected by the patriarch of Ferney, whom he always refers to as 'de Voltaire'. The two only met once, shortly before Voltaire's death.

Beyond the Genevans Diderot was in touch with the enlightened aristocracy and the republic of letters all over Europe. In Paris he received the visits of German princelings and saw Englishmen such as Wilkes, Sterne, and Hume (usually at the Baron's dinner-table). But his most important foreign tie was with Saint Petersburg. For mixed reasons, Catherine the Great had shown interest in the *Encyclopédie* when it was meeting with persecution in France and had even suggested that the whole enterprise be transported to Russia. In 1765, in order to give Diderot financial help, she bought his library, giving him the use of it during his lifetime. In return, as well as singing her praises, he acted as picture-buyer for the Empress; in this capacity he had many dealings with the Russian ambassador Prince Golitsyn, who subsequently appears as ambassador at the Hague, where he was Diderot's host in 1773 and 1774. This was the philosopher's first sight of the sea and the first stage of his longest journey. At the age of 60 he travelled by post-chaise from Paris to Saint Petersburg and stayed there for several months, living on familiar terms with Catherine, seeing her sometimes for several hours a day and returning to Paris much aged, but full of enthusiasm for this Semiramis of the North.

Of the groups of actors in these letters we have still to introduce the most important, the Volland family. Sophie's father, Jean-Robert Volland, had been a civil servant; he had a house in Paris, in the Rue des Vieux-Augustins, and a country house at Isle-sur-Marne, something over a hundred miles east of Paris. He died in 1752 or 1753, leaving a widow and three daughters. Madame Volland, whom Diderot calls 'Morphyse', appears in these letters as a vigorous old lady and a vigilant obstacle to the love of Sophie and the philosopher. In spite of this she and Diderot respected one another and he acted rather like a son-in-law towards her. As time goes on he tends to write of her with greater affection; instead of 'Morphyse' she becomes 'mama'. Her oldest daughter, born in 1715, was married to a financial official of the Duke of Orleans known as Monsieur de Salignac; they lived in Paris in the Rue Saint-Thomas-du-Louvre. In 1762 Salignac went bankrupt in scandalous circumstances and disappeared from sight; his wife came to live with her family under the new name of Madame de Blacy. Diderot often refers to her jokingly as 'my sweetheart'. She had two children, a son called Vallet de Fayolle who made a career in the colonies after his father's ruin, and a daughter Mélanie, who was blind.

Madame Volland's second daughter was baptized in 1716 as Louise-Henriette. For us she is Sophie, a name she probably received from Diderot. She is also addressed in these letters as 'Mademoiselle' or 'Mademoiselle Volland'. She never married and died in 1784, shortly before her lover. Virtually all we know about her is contained in these letters; it would be presumptuous to attempt to deduce from them a 'character'. There is some uncertainty about the beginning of her relationship with Diderot; it is not even certain that they were lovers in the modern sense of the word, though anyone who reads these letters will find it hard to doubt it. They appear to have met in 1755; between that time and 1759, Diderot wrote 134 letters to Sophie, all of which were lost or destroyed. He speaks of a 'little staircase' which led him to her at this time, but it was evidently difficult for them to be alone together. When the first surviving letter was written, Sophie (who was already 42) had just been carried off to Isle by her mother after being found in a *tête-à-tête* with Diderot. This was to be the pattern of their life. The jealous Morphyse stood guard over her daughter and year by year took her off to spend the long summer months (sometimes even the winter) in the country. To this we owe most of the *Letters to Sophie Volland*. Between 1768 and 1770, Diderot had a last love-affair, with Madame d'Épinay's friend Madame de Maux; at the same time his love for Sophie cooled into something more like an affectionate philosophical friendship. From this time on his letters were addressed to all the Volland ladies, not just Sophie. But in her will she left him her seven volumes of Montaigne and the ring she called her 'pauline'.

Morphyse's third daughter also bore a nickname; considerably younger than Sophie, she is 'Uranie' or 'little sister', Marie-Charlotte, the wife of a disagreeable architect and engineer named Le Gendre. They lived for much of the time in Châlons-sur-Marne, but in 1766 Le Gendre bought a Paris house in the Rue Sainte-Anne. Marie-Charlotte was a tease; Diderot's letters tell of a succession of unfortunate suitors, Marzon, Vialet and Perronet (both colleagues of her husband), and then the tutor Digeon, who managed his affairs well and married her daughter after her death in 1768. It will be seen that Diderot's feelings towards Uranie were complex; he was attracted to her, flirted with her at times, but was driven into frenzies of jealousy by the love between the two sisters. His letters show surprisingly little reaction to her sudden death.

As for the friends of the Vollands, we know almost nothing about them. There is a Vallet de Villeneuve, nephew to Monsieur de Salignac, whom we see in 1760 attempting to despoil the Volland ladies of debts left by his father; he also appears on one occasion at La Chevrette. Then there are Monsieur de Prysie, Mademoiselle Boileau, Monsieur and Madame Bouchard, Monsieur Gaschon, and other shadowy figures whose lives and characters we can invent for ourselves on the strength of Diderot's passing remarks. The striking thing is the separation of the two worlds, the solid upper bourgeoisie of the Vollands and the high society of the Paris intellectuals. Sophie never went to Le Grandval—but then neither did Madame Diderot.

* * *

The letters to Sophie originally formed a numbered series from 1 to 553. Of these 189 survive, together with a few fragments preserved by Diderot's disciple Naigeon for their philosophical value. In this volume I have included almost no fragments, since for all their interest these detached thoughts would be too much like a 'wit and wisdom of Diderot'. Complete letters give a truer impression of the living reality. I have chosen letters from all periods, although the weight of the correspondence falls most heavily on the years 1759–62. For certain periods (1763–4, 1771–2, after 1774) there are no surviving letters, partly because in those years Diderot was less separated from Sophie. One day I should like to translate the complete body of letters; a selection inevitably makes what is chosen more difficult to follow, but as far as possible I have picked letters which elucidate one another.

Diderot dated his letters spasmodically and often incorrectly; I have eliminated his dates from the text and dated all the letters as accurately as possible. Where he divides his letters into paragraphs I have followed his division; otherwise I have made my own (in this case the paragraphs are usually longer). I have taken account of his punctuation, particularly in the rendering of dialogue, which is sometimes unfaithfully transcribed in French editions. The spelling of proper names has been standardized in accordance with modern practice.

I am grateful for having been given the opportunity to read the originals of these letters, which are bound up in two fine volumes in the manuscript room of the Bibliothèque Nationale, Paris. In reading them I was able to correct a few mistakes in existing editions. I must however acknowledge my debt to André Babelon, who first published the letters from the original manuscripts, to Monsieur Yves Florenne, who has edited a handsome volume for the Club Français du Livre, and in particular to Monsieur Georges Roth, whose learned edition of Diderot's correspondence is published by the Éditions de Minuit. Finally I want to thank my wife Siân, who has made many suggestions for improving my versions. It was she who first had the idea of this translation; to her I dedicate this volume.

# DIDEROT'S LETTERS TO SOPHIE VOLLAND

1

*Paris, 11 May 1759*

*Friday morning*

At eight o'clock yesterday morning we set out for Marly. We arrived at half past ten. We ordered a large dinner and wandered out into the park, where I was impressed by the contrast between the delicate art of the pavilions and arbours and the natural wildness of a dense mass of tall trees towering in the background. These pavilions, set far apart and half hidden by forest, seem the dwellings of subordinate sprites, whose master lives in the central one. All this gave the place a fairy-tale feeling which pleased me.

A garden should not have too many statues; I think this one is a little too full of them. Statues should be thought of as beings who love solitude and search after it, poets, philosophers, and lovers—and such beings are rare. Let there be no more than a few beautiful statues, hidden from one another in the remotest places; either they will beckon to me or else I shall seek them out, or perhaps come on them by chance; they will stop me and we shall have long talks together. I want no more statues than that.

I wandered aimlessly through the park in a melancholy frame of mind. The others had gone striding on ahead of us and we followed slowly, the Baron von Gleichen and I.[1] I was happy to be with the baron, for we both felt within us the same secret emotion. It is strange how sensitive spirits can understand each other almost without speaking. A chance word, a fit of absent-mindedness, a vague disjointed remark, a passing regret, an ambiguous expression, a tone of voice, a way of walking, a look, a moment of attention or of silence, all these give them away to one another. We said little; we felt a lot; we were both suffering; but he was more to be pitied than I. I looked from time to time towards the city; his eyes were often fixed on the ground; he was searching for one who no longer exists.

We came to a piece of sculpture which struck me by its

[1] Baron von Gleichen, born in 1735, was the envoy in Paris of the Margrave of Bayreuth. His wife had died not long before this letter was written.

simplicity and the force and sublimity of its theme—a Centaur carrying a child on its back. The child is holding out his little fingers towards the fierce animal's head and leading him by a hair. You should see the Centaur's face, the way he holds his head, his gentle expression, his respect for the infant tyrant, at whom he looks as if he were afraid to move. Another statue gave me even greater pleasure, an old faun holding a newborn child lovingly in his arms. The statue of Agrippina bathing is not equal to its reputation, or perhaps I was badly placed to judge it properly.

We divided our walk into two parts. We visited the lower part of the park before dinner. Everyone had a good appetite for dinner. Our own dear Baron was madder than ever. There is something original both in his ideas and in his way of talking. Imagine a merry, witty, indecent, robust satyr among a group of soft, chaste, delicate figures. That is how he seemed in our midst. He would not have embarrassed or offended my Sophie, because my Sophie can be either man or woman as she chooses. He would not have embarrassed or offended my friend Grimm, because Grimm lets imagination run free and only dislikes wit when it is clumsily handled. Oh, how we missed our friend Grimm! What a sweet moment it was in our meal when our souls opened out and we began to evoke and praise our absent friends! What warmth of feelings and ideas! What enthusiasm! What pleasure it gave us to speak of them! How glad they would have been to hear us! Dear Grimm, who will pass my words on to you?

Our dinner was long, yet it seemed short. We visited the upper part of the park. I observed that of all water decorations, there are none so beautiful as those which fall continuously or flow—and there were none of these in the park. We talked of art, of poetry, of philosophy, and of love; of the greatness and vanity of our undertakings; of the bittersweet thoughts of immortality; of men, of gods, and of kings; of space and time; of death and life. All this made a harmony in which the dissonances of our Baron constantly stood out. Then the wind got up, the evening grew cold, and we came back to our carriage.

The Baron von Gleichen has travelled a great deal. He entertained us on the return journey, telling us of the State Inquisitors of Venice, who always walk between the confessor and the executioner, of the barbarity of the Sicilian court, which handed over an ancient triumphal chariot, with its bas-reliefs and its horses, to some monks who have melted it all down for bells. We were led on to this by the demolition of a cascade at Marly to provide marble for chapel walls in Saint-Sulpice. I said little. I listened and daydreamed. Between eight and nine we got out at our friend's door. I rested there till ten.

I fell asleep from weariness and unhappiness. Yes, my dear, unhappiness. I fear the worst for the future. Your mother's soul is sealed with the seven seals of the Apocalypse. On her forehead is written: *mystery*. I saw two sphinxes at Marly and that reminded me of her. She has promised us, indeed she has promised herself more than she can keep. But then I console myself with the lifegiving certainty that nothing can separate our two souls. People have so often said that, written it, and sworn it. This once at least let it be true. If it is not, I shall not be to blame, Sophie.

Monsieur de Saint-Lambert has invited the Baron and me to go and spend a few days at Épinay with Madame d'Houdetot. I said no, and I was right to, wasn't I? Woe to the man who seeks distractions! He will find them and his affliction will be cured, whereas I want to keep mine until the time when everything comes to an end. I am afraid of coming to see you, but I must; fate treats us as if unhappiness were necessary to create a lasting bond between us.

Goodbye, my dear. Please send me a note by way of Lanau.

By the way, don't impose too much on your sister's goodwill; only talk to her about us when you cannot contain your feelings, or when she asks you to. Our friends, even our dearest friends, cannot attach much importance to such matters. You need to have learnt to listen to lovers and pity them. She does not yet know this art; may she never learn it!

I kiss the ring you have worn.

## 2

*Paris, 2 June 1759*

*Saturday morning*

My good and tenderhearted friend, here is the work of the great sophist.[1] I have not read it. I do not yet feel serene enough to judge it impartially. It is better to put it off than to rush into committing an injustice. Keep a watch on your heart too and do not let your displeasure with the man affect your judgement of the author. Listen to him as if I had no grievance against him.

So it is possible to be a man of eloquence and feeling without possessing any of the principles of honour, true friendship, virtue, or truthfulness? This really distresses me. If the fellow has not got a ready-made system of moral depravity in his head, how I pity him! And if he has invented notions of justice and injustice to match his evil dealings, how much the more do I pity him! Everything hangs together in the fabric of morality. It is difficult for a man to keep on writing paradoxes and remain simple in his behaviour. Look into your heart, my Sophie, and tell me why you are so sincere, so open and so truthful in all you say? It is because these same qualities are the foundation of your character and your actions. It would indeed be strange if a man could be evil in all his thoughts and words, but good in all his actions. The disorder of the head influences the heart and the disorder of the heart affects the head.

My dear, let us live in such a way that our life may be free from falsehood. The more highly I regard you, the dearer you will be to me. The more virtuously I behave, the more you will love me. How I should shun vice, even if I had no other judge than my Sophie! I have set up in her heart a statue which I hope I shall never break. How it would pain her if I were guilty of an action which debased me in her eyes! Is it not true that you would rather see me dead than an evil-doer? Love me then always, so that I may always shun vice. Continue to uphold me on the road of goodness. How sweet it is to open your arms to welcome and clasp to yourself a good man! It is this thought which sanctifies our kisses; what are the kisses of two lovers when they do not express the infinitely high esteem in which they hold one another? How petty and miserable are the raptures of ordinary lovers! How charming, exalted, and passionate our embraces! Come, my Sophie, come. I feel my heart warm to you. That emotion which enhances your beauty is about to shine on my face. Now I can feel it. Oh, how I wish you were here to take pleasure in it! If you could see me now, how happy you would be! How touched

[1] Jean-Jacques Rousseau's *Lettre à d'Alembert*.

you would be if you could see the tears in my eyes and the expression on my face! Oh, why do they insist on standing in the way of two beings whose happiness heaven was glad to contemplate? They do not know all the harm they are doing; we must forgive them.

I shall not see you this morning. I should not find Monsieur Petit at home, and I am delayed here by Monsieur de Chimène. I have spent the night reading his tragedy and making a synopsis of it for Grimm.[1] Tonight I am going to the new comedy, and that too is for Grimm. What a beautiful trio of souls, yours, mine, and his! If I were to lose one of the other two, what could fill that terrible gap? Live then, both of you, if you do not want me one day to be a voice crying in the wilderness.

I shall be in the pit, fairly well back and in the middle; from there I shall look out for you. I shall come home after the short play, or even before it, to get my ideas down on paper—that is the task imposed on me by my friend.

Tomorrow at midday I shall be where you expect me. I shall be there without fail. How many sweet moments I must sacrifice for your mother! I have been thinking about your sister's reluctance. So she doesn't think highly enough of me to want to be shut up in the same locket? But that's not the reason, my Sophie. Perhaps she is afraid that one day, when you are still alive or when you are dead, that locket. . . . So your mother will stand in the way of all the sweet, innocent things we plan? Tell your sister that the two portraits can be arranged as she likes . . . tell her that I am a decent man, that nothing will make me change towards you . . . tell her that I am certain of a great reputation with posterity . . . tell her that I have reached an age where a man's character is fixed . . . tell her how flattered I should be and how happy you would be to have us both, to feel us both with you, to see her with me and me with her. . . conjure up for her the moment when you will separate, she to return to Châlons, you to come back to Paris. . . . To refuse you her portrait is to show that she is not attached to yours. . . .

Madam,[2] think carefully and do not grieve your sister. Follow the impulses of your soul; it will always guide you well. I like

[1] The tragedy was entitled *Don Carlos*.

[2] This paragraph is addressed to Madame Le Gendre, whose portrait Sophie intended to place in a locket with that of Diderot.

it when people show delicacy of feeling. I also like it if they ignore such things occasionally. . . . It is enough to be able to say to yourself in the future: 'I had thought of that.' . . . It is strange that it should be a jealous man talking and insisting in this way. Am I blasé? I don't know. I only feel that I desire something strongly which would have pained me if it had happened without my consent. It would have pained me a great deal, but I desire it strongly; and it is a favour for which I should be infinitely grateful to Madame Le Gendre, because it is a way of obliging you which you would prefer to any other.

If your sister agrees to our request and you have both our portraits, take care, Sophie and do not look more tenderly at her than at me. Do not kiss her more often. If you do, I shall find out.

Goodbye, my dear, until tomorrow. Oh what a lovely evening we had yesterday! You were so loving and tender and Mademoiselle Boileau talked so delightfully. She was happy at your happiness and at mine. That is the mark of a sweet character.

## 3

*Langres, 3 August 1759*

Here is my fourth letter, my dear. The first one was sent directly to you; the second, in a separate envelope, was addressed to the office of Monsieur Berger, the Salt Tax Superintendent, and the third to Madame Le Gendre.

I have had three letters from you; two of them arrived together. My brother opened the last one, but he only read a few lines of it and luckily there was nothing in them to shock him; it was where you were telling me about the little girl's latest illness. Give me my title of Academician of Berlin in future so as to avoid a confusion which would upset the man of God.

Poor child,[1] how sorry I feel for her—and for her mother! They will say that the child's suffering was needed to demonstrate the mother's tender love. What nonsense! An innocent and delicate creature has to be sacrificed in order to display the compassion of another; she has to be made to weep and groan

[1] Émilie, Madame Le Gendre's daughter.

and they both have to be made miserable so that one of them may be seen to be good; injustice has to be done so that virtue can have its day; we have to incur reproach so as to make ouselves worthy of praise; and we have to degrade ourselves in our eyes so as to win honour in the eyes of our fellow-men and even of ourselves. What a system! What would anyone think of a ruler who governed his country in this fashion? Are there two justices, one for Heaven and one for Earth? In that case, what happens to the notion of justice? If the child dies, her short life will have been nothing but suffering. If she survives, she will still have been punished before committing any crime. But her father has sinned, even if she hasn't, they will say. The fools! They don't see that this answer comes from the fable of the lamb and the wolf who were drinking side by side from the same stream, and that the god they worship is the wolf; and without this fable, cries sublime Pascal, the universe is an incomprehensible enigma —and your fable is a blasphemy, is my reply.

Now that the glass is broken on your picture, I have to purse up my lips; I put my fingers to my mouth and I blow you kisses, as Émilie does to her mama. We shall soon be together again, my dear, never fear, and these lips will once again touch the lips I love. Until then I forbid your mouth to everyone except your sister. It does not make me unhappy to be her successor, indeed it rather pleases me. It is as if I were pressing her soul between yours and mine. She is like a snowflake which will perhaps melt away between two coals of fire. How sweet she was on the day we parted! How she sympathized with our unhappiness! She was quite downcast. You didn't notice that almost all the colour had gone from her cheeks. I did though; when I recall it, I say to myself: If ever she loves a man, how well he will be loved! How we shall suffer, my Sophie and I, if ever we are present at their parting! Speak well of me to her. What she will most like to hear and what will make her think most highly of me and be the best justification of her feelings towards me, is that you love me, that I am madly in love with you, and that my love will never change, so keep telling her this from morning to night.

I am very glad that Gaschon is better and that his rival is the sort of man to be satisfied with a maxim from the opera. That's all the affair is worth.

I don't know why you haven't had my letters yet. Send me a word of reassurance.

There is a charming walk here. It is a long avenue of leafy trees leading to a clump of trees grouped together without any sort of order or symmetry. It is a cool solitary place. You go down some rustic steps to a spring which gushes out of a rock. The water collects in a basin, then flows out and forms a pool; it runs on down and fills up a second pool, then is channelled down to a third pool with a fountain in the middle. The basin and the three pools are placed one below the other, quite far apart, on a long slope. The last one is surrounded by old lime trees which are in flower now. Between the lime trees there are stone seats. That is where you will find me at five o'clock. I let my eyes wander over the loveliest of landscapes. There is a line of hills with houses and gardens scattered over them, and down below a winding stream which waters the meadows and then gathers the water from the spring and various other little streams and flows on down to the plain. I spend hours there reading, thinking, contemplating nature, and dreaming of my love. How I wish there were three of us on that stone seat! It is the haunt of the local young lovers, and mine too. They go there in the evening, when the end of the day releases them from work and brings them together. The days must seem very long to them and the evenings very short. While I sit there, my brother, my sister, and a friend are sorting out money matters. I am longing for them to have finished.

Here is a little story which I found touching—and you will too. My father was friendly with a woman, a relation of his, poor, a good soul, and about the same age as him. They fell ill at the same time. My father died on Whitsunday. She learned of his death and died the following day. My sister closed her eyes and they were buried side by side.

'Closed her eyes' would be a figure of speech in Paris; here it is a real act of kindness. My sister was telling me yesterday how a son who was by his father's deathbed thought the time had come to do him this last service. He was wrong. His father felt his hand, opened his eyes and said: 'Wait a moment, son.'

Oh what a task my father has left me, my dear, if I want ever to win the sort of honour which is accorded to his memory! There is only one poor portrait here of this excellent man, but I am not to blame for this. If he had been well enough to come to Paris, I had intended to have him painted at his work-bench in his working clothes, bare-headed and looking up to the heavens, with his hand raised in a blessing over his grand-daughter's forehead.

We shall all shut one another's eyes in our little castle and the last one will be the one to be pitied, won't he?

Since I came away from this town, everyone I knew has died. The only acquaintance I have found still alive is a woman who was the friend of a girl I once loved—she is dead now. I was very happy to see this woman again. We talked a little of old times. I must tell you something about her which will move you. Not long after the death of our friend, I was here on a visit. One day as I was coming out of our house she came out of hers. She asked me to accompany her to the church and I gave her my arm. When we got to the cemetery, she turned her head away and pointed to the place where the one we had both loved was lying. Imagine the effect her silence and her gesture had on me.

I feel rather more at peace with myself now. I have done the good work which I intended. I have reconciled my brother and my sister, we have all embraced, they have mingled their tears. They are going to live together; I only hope they will make one another happy! And why shouldn't they? They are both tender-hearted and kind. But is that enough? I do my best not to notice the difference in their characters; otherwise I should leave here very despondent.

Goodbye, my dear. Dear sister, look after her health—and do not neglect your own too much. All my best wishes for the dear child. When I hear from you I shall write to your mother. Goodbye, goodbye.

Remember me to the Abbé,[1] and to Messieurs Gaschon and de Prysie. Say whatever you like on my behalf to Mademoiselle Boileau; I am sure to agree with you. And what has become of her plans? She is avoiding you. I am sure she has still just as high a regard for you—and for herself.

I still haven't heard from Grimm. What is he doing? What

[1] Often mentioned in these letters, this is Abbé Le Monnier, a friend of the Volland family and correspondent of Diderot. He was a poet and translator and chaplain at the Sainte Chapelle in Paris.

can he be thinking of? Is he well? Is he ill? I don't know what to make of his silence. He can't possibly think I am still in Paris.

Goodbye, my dear; I put my lips to yours and kiss them, even if your sister's kisses are still there. But no, there's nothing there; hers are so light and airy.

## 4

*Langres, 11 August 1759*

*Saturday*

Here are the details of my domestic peace treaty. It seemed to me that my sister was rather tired of managing household affairs and that her economic principles did not suit the Abbé. The Abbé wants to spend and his sister wants to save. The Abbé likes plenty of company and good food. Little sister prefers small gatherings and hospitality which is decent rather than lavish. In the course of his ecclesiastical rounds the Abbé has made all sorts of friends and acquaintances, who will use him as he used them. Little sister can see the house becoming a sort of hostelry and she is afraid that she will be the one to bear the burden of housekeeping, never having any peace, frittering away their income, and being constantly surrounded by a lot of unknown and unpleasant faces. It is nice to hear her describing all these people she has never set eyes on and giving her own imaginary version of their conversations. One of the things about her is her sprightly bad temper; she makes you laugh when she is cross. When she has had her say and everyone has laughed she thinks she has won the day and feels satisfied.

So what did I do then? I started by persuading the Abbé out of the jealous idea he had somehow got into his head that I liked my sister better than him. I tried to convince him that even if I loved her a hundred times more than he supposed, there was still something I loved better, and that was justice. I was careful not to rub him up the wrong way. I steered clear of anything which might have hurt his feelings. I won his confidence; then I set to work. Little sister had a friend who was badly off. I persuaded her to get her friend to live with her; the Abbé agreed. She is settled in now; she looks after the housekeeping and little sister doesn't have to bother herself with it any more than she wants to. This means that they have to pay for the keep of the friend's niece who was living with her aunt and who had to be sent to live in a suitable safe place, but what does that matter? Not a bit. Then I had to arrange the joint expenditure so that the Abbé could spend as much as he wanted and his sister save as much as she wanted, without either of them seeming a burden to the other. I suggested to the Abbé that his sister should pay him a regular allowance. They both agreed. I fixed the allowance and that is the end of that.

Of the three houses we had, we have decided to sell one. The other two are in the town and the country respectively. They will live in the town house. It will be their property; and they will pay me a third of its value. The country house will be the common property of all three of us. It will be the storehouse for our wine crop and our corn harvest. The proceeds have been divided into three shares. They offered me the first share, which I am sure is the best. I am not concerned about the money, but I like generous actions and I can't tell you how touched I was by their generosity. They drew lots for the other two shares. In any case these divisions are more apparent than real; they are just reasonable precautions against future difficulties. Our income will continue to come in together. My brother and sister will administer affairs and every year I shall be sent my share, which will vary according to whether the year has been good or bad. This way we shall insure one another against accidents. The hail will fall on us all equally; we shall prosper together and suffer together. Our possessions are separate; each of us has his own, but we all stand together against misfortune. Dear father! if you could be with your children in spirit, how happy you would be!

All this took no more than a quarter of an hour, and it all passed off so easily and calmly and decently that you would both have wept with joy to see it. I didn't want there to be any question about the furniture. Little sister and the Abbé will share it between them. But I suspect them of making up for this by adding to my share. I have dealt well with them, as they have with me. We have sold off some useless items, various debtors have paid up and others will pay before long. Money which was due has been coming in; we have a common purse which is growing fatter daily; when all that was owing to us has come in, we shall open it and share out its contents, once my father's last wishes have been carried out. There are many other little details which show the same spirit and which I would tell you about if I could remember them; you would find them interesting because you love me. The act of division has just been brought to me. It has been drawn up by an honest man. We shall copy it and sign it, then we shall embrace and say goodbye.

I look forward to that moment with trepidation. So do my brother and sister. We had decided on Monday, but they asked me to stay a few days longer. How could I refuse? It may be a long time before they see me again. I only hope your good mother will forgive the delay. I expect she will. The Abbé wanted to take me off to his priory. One of my friends who lived in the forests had ventured out to see me. I had promised him a visit but the Abbé changed his mind, so I shall have to let my friend down. I regret every day I am forced to spend away from you. I also regret the letter which is waiting for me at Isle. Your mother has it now and it will stay too long in her keeping. How will she hand it over to me? And how shall I take it? We shall both be embarrassed. She will see my embarrassment and I shall guess hers; neither of us will say a word, or if we do speak, I am sure to stammer—and I don't like stammering. And do you think I will dare ask for pen and ink to write to you? You know what I am!

The people who live round here are very quick-witted, rather too lively, and as fickle as weathervanes. I think this is due to the changeable weather, which can go from cold to hot, from calm to stormy, or from fair to rainy in twenty-four hours; this is bound to affect them and stop their minds ever remaining steady for more than twenty-four hours at a stretch. From the cradle up they get used to turning with every wind that blows. The head of a man from Langres is as firm on his shoulders as the cock on a church steeple. It never stays fixed in one direction; and if ever it comes back to its original position, it does not stay there for long. But in spite of this amazing rapidity in their movements, their desires, their plans, their whims, and their ideas, they have a slow way of talking. My sister is very likely the only person in the town who speaks quickly. I don't know the reason for this exception, but certainly to listen to her you would take her for a foreigner to these parts.

As for me, I am a true man of Langres, except that life in the capital and my own efforts have corrected me a little. I am constant in my tastes. When I have once come to like something I go on liking it, because my preferences always have a reason. Whether I love or hate, I always know the reason why. It is true that I am naturally inclined to overlook faults and be carried away by good qualities. The charms of virtue affect me more strongly than the horrors of vice. I turn quietly away from the evil and cling to the good. If there is a beautiful side to a book, a character, a painting, or a statue, I let my eyes dwell on it. I neither see nor remember anything else. The rest is as good as forgotten. What then when the whole is beautiful? You know, my Sophie, so do you, her sister, and you, my friend. It is unity that makes up the beauty of the whole. Seen in this light, Cromwell is beautiful, and Scipio too, and Medea and Aria and Caesar and Brutus.

There's a scrap of philosophy which I let slip. It can be the text for one of our chats on our bench in the Palais-Royal.

Goodbye, my dear. Eight days from now and I shall be there, I hope. I shall no longer need to write that I love you; I shall say it to you, swear it to you; you will see the truth of what I say and you will be happy and so shall I—and won't your dear sister be happy too?

## 5

*Isle, 18 August 1759*

Here I am at last, mademoiselle, in the house where I have been so long awaited. Your dear mama was very much inclined to scold me; in other words she was very anxious to get back to you, but you also know how kind and understanding she is. I gave her my reasons for being late, she accepted them and everything was all right.

It was about six o'clock when the chaise turned into the drive. I told the driver to stop. I got down. I went to meet her with outstretched arms and she welcomed me as you know she always welcomes those whom she is glad to see. We talked for a few minutes in the disconnected way which is inevitable on such occasions. 'I was expecting you the other day.' 'I hoped to get here then, but I couldn't.' 'And the next day?' 'How could I refuse a brother and a sister who asked for just one more day?' 'Was it very hot travelling?' 'Yes, especially after Perthes, as I had the sun in my eyes.' 'Are you very tired?' 'A little.' 'You look healthy.' 'I think you are looking better.' 'And your business?' 'All done. All done.' 'But perhaps you would like to rest; come with me, I will show you your room.'

I gave her my arm and was led to the room with the harpsichord; I stayed there a little and then came back to the drawing room where I found your dear mother working with Mademoiselle Desmarets. The sun had set. It was a beautiful evening. We made the most of it. First of all we made a tour of the ground floor. I had liked the look of the house from outside; the inside was just as good. The drawing room in particular is perfect. I like wood panelling, particularly if it is simple, as this is. The air must be good here, for the wood seemed to be quite intact. And then the three doors leading out to the drive, the garden and the *vordes*![1] It would be impossible to improve on it. If Madame Le Gendre needs more than this in our little castle, she must have a depraved taste for luxury. Yes, madam, you who have such a sensitive and tender soul, you who take such delight in hearing of virtuous words and good deeds, throw your cushions out of the window and win one blessing more.

Next we looked all over the big courtyard which is to the right of the house, with the barns, the farmyards, the grapestore, the winepress, the sheepfolds, and the stables. I said it gave me great pleasure to see all these places, as indeed it did, because they interest me. The old patriarchs, whose history it is impossible to read without feeling nostalgia for their lost way of life, had only tents and stables to live in. They had nothing resembling a sofa, nothing but fresh clean hay and they led fine healthy lives, surrounded by hordes of children.

Mama is as agile as a hare. She has no fear of brambles, thorns, and dunghills. These things do not stop her, nor me either; they do not offend her nostrils, nor mine either. Believe me, to an honest nose, which has not lost its natural innocence, it's not the goat but the woman drenched in musk and amber who stinks. That's a brutal way of putting it, but it is true.

[1] Plantations of poplars, sallows, or willows, or a mixture of the three.

While we were out there, the carts of hay and grain were coming in, and I liked that too. Oh, I am a true rustic, and proud of it, ladies. Then we walked round the garden, which seemed small to me. I was misled by that gate at the end of it, opposite the drawing room; I didn't know that it led out to the *vordes*, or even that they were *vordes*. We walked through them and over the two bridges. I greeted the Marne again, my compatriot and faithful travelling companion.

Those *vordes* are truly charming. That would be the place for me to live and dream and feel gentle emotions and say soft words and love tenderly; there I would sacrifice to Pan and the Venus of the fields, at the foot of every tree even, if I were given leave and time enough. You will say perhaps that there are many trees, but when I promise myself a happy life, it is a long life too. What a beautiful place the *vordes* are! When you remember them, how can you endure the sight of your symmetrical Tuileries, or the tedious walks of the Palais-Royal, where all your trees are cut down to cabbage tops and where you still stifle, however hard they may have tried to give you some air and space by pruning and cutting, and smashing and disfiguring?

What are you doing now, where are you? You would do much better to come here than to make us come to you. There is a sublimity about these *vordes* and all such places planted by nature which is turned to prettiness by man's improving hand. Oh hand of man, what sacrilege you committed when you laid down the spade and began to trifle with gold and precious stones!

I have seen the place; we have sat there and talked there, in the little summerhouse which you have consecrated with your thoughts; for they tell me it was there, madam, that you would go to be alone with yourself. Come and take refuge there once more. The mortal who most admires and respects you will pass by without breaking in on you. Come! A mere moment in this solitary place will show you that the eternal being who gives life to the nature that surrounds you, if he exists, is good and cares much more for the purity of our souls than the truth of our opinions. Why! What does it matter to him what we think about him, provided that our lives show him that we are his disciples and his children? Come; you will not be disturbed; my profane Sophie and I will stray far off; we shall wait for a sign before we approach Uranie. And all the while, dear mama will guard the happiness of the one who meditates and of the two who are wandering. You see what living in the country does for me. I am happy with what I write, or rather I write and I am happy, whereas in town, instead of surrendering myself to the charms of nature, I should probably spend my time making subtle distinctions between the words hypocrisy and falsehood.

It was rather late when we came in. The dew, to which you may be a stranger, moistens the plants at nightfall and refreshes them after the heat of the day. If it had not been for that, we should perhaps have stayed out longer. We rested a little in the drawing room. During the evening I told your mother about my domestic arrangements. We spoke of her darling daughters and exchanged some tender words about the young mother and her child. I described them to her as they were during that time when it was so overpoweringly hot and the mother took her burning and feverish child into her arms and held her to her breast for hours together; and I saw the tears in her eyes, and we said; 'Having done her duty so well, she must be so pleased with herself that the memory of it will be enough to console her.'

I told your dear mama that I was anxious about your health, and she gave me two of your letters. Today I have just received a third together with pens, ink, and paper for me to answer it, but I am not doing so. I am leaving everything else on one side in order to tell you how happy I am to be in a place where you have lived. Shall we never all come together to live here in peace and harmony? Here it is, the little dream castle, all ready for us.

We went to bed early. The bed seemed excellent to me, and I should have slept very well if it hadn't been for you. But that decree,[1] which I hadn't heard about, kept running through my mind and stopped me sleeping. If you weren't in Paris, I should try to forget about the place. In addition to this business, there is all the grief surrounding you, which is magnified by my imagination, and then there is Monsieur de Prysie's brother, and all the other victims, and the nation, and the taxes. Even so we

[1] After the decree of March 1759 forbidding the publication of subsequent volumes of the *Encyclopédie*, there was a further order on 21 July 1759, stating that subscribers should be reimbursed for the volumes not yet published. In the event, no subscriber took advantage of this.

are coming back to that home of disorder and distress. Châlons tomorrow, where Monsieur Le Gendre is expecting us, and on Tuesday morning, I hope, Paris, which in spite of all the harsh things I think and say about it, is still the home of happiness for me. Until Tuesday then, madam; until Tuesday, mademoiselle; on Tuesday I shall bring your dear mama back to you—how that will make you love me! Dear, hospitable mama came and spent the morning with me talking about you; which was just what I had been wanting. On the road to Paris we shall often come back to a subject which is equally near to both our hearts.

Since I have a few moments to spare, I will reply to your letters, mademoiselle. Don't complain about our lack of eagerness to get back to you, unless at the same time you send us wings. I have indeed tasted all the pleasures you describe, but even so I am nowhere near as flourishing as you imagine. I am quite well though and I hope to make up for lost time without endangering my health.

But talking of work, the publishers' latest troubles, which will discourage them still more, will possibly have the effect of leaving me unemployed. But there might be more gain than loss in that, as dear mama conclusively proved to me, and then she went on: 'This decree is perhaps no more than a rumour; you know Mademoiselle Volland, reporting isn't her strong point.' And I go along with her ideas because they comfort me and I value my peace of mind—as you know, though you often take pleasure in robbing me of it. Without knowing any of the details of our misfortune, we have been able to imagine the despondency it has caused, but you are there, you can see it all, and that's quite a different matter. Soon we shall be as unhappy as you are, but not in the first moments of meeting. How sweet those moments will be! How we have longed for them!

I do not think the plan to reduce luxury, to bring back the taste for useful things, and to turn people's minds towards trade, agriculture, and population is as difficult or as dangerous as you imagine. And even if it had some temporary drawbacks, what does it matter? You cannot cure a sick man without hurting him, making him cry out, and even mutilating him sometimes.

I am glad to hear that Madame Le Gendre is recovering. If life is a bad thing, at least reason, which teaches us to bear its tribulations, is a good thing. Keep up your walks in the Palais-Royal.

Distract your dear sister and distract yourself. Summon me occasionally to the bench in the Allé e d'Argenson and tell the people sitting there that it belongs to dear mama and they must make way.

Yes, my Sophie, yes, I shall always love those walks; yes, they will begin again, we shall bare our souls and whether or not we like what we find there, at least we shall know that we have hidden nothing from one another. Is yours still as pure as before? If there were something in it which called for my forgiveness, I should give it of course, but it would cost me a great deal. I am so used to your innocence. That is a strange way of talking. But why is it that all our most decent expressions have become almost ridiculous? Really we have ruined everything, even our language and the words we use. There must be an oil-stain which has seeped from the middle to the very edge of the cloth.

This brings me to the decree of the Council. Our enemies really are extraordinary, so persistent and venomous! Truly when I compare our loves with our hates, the loves appear frail and small and feeble. We know how to hate, but not how to love; and am I the one who says so, my Sophie, I of all people? Could it really be the truth then?

As for the rumour that I had gone off to Holland, that David had gone on ahead, and that we were going to finish our work there, it is just what I expected. You can doubt anything you like, my lady Sceptic, as long as you believe in my tender feelings for you. They are as genuine as on the first day.

Your Latin quotation is very funny. I must have a twisted mind, I see innuendo everywhere. I have received everything you sent and in good time. We are spending the day here. It began very pleasantly, as I said. Tomorrow we shall take a dose of mass at Vitry and spend the rest of the day in your dear sister's home. I love places where those who are dear to me have been; I love to touch the things that have surrounded them and to breathe the air they have breathed. Would you even be jealous of the air?

You forgive me for letting a post go without writing to you, and that can't be very difficult for you. What's more, it's the usual story. You are always ready to forgive precisely the crimes which I haven't committed. How vehemently your sister accuses me! How well and expressively she talks! How eloquent and passionate she would be if she were to fall in love! But whether fortunately or unfortunately, the extraordinary being who could win her love has yet to be born. I did not commit any follies in Langres. Don't worry; I sometimes smiled at things that were said, but that was as far as it went. You say you have seen the Baron at the Palais-Royal; he must be in Paris then. The man is always on the move; he is not at peace within himself, so he feels at home nowhere. I really should have written to tell him of my departure, my stay in Langres, my business affairs, the life I have been leading, and my return to Paris. Everything went to Grimm and Sophie, but perhaps he didn't even notice? There are times when I worry about things which no one else is aware of.

Why this curiosity about Grimm's letter? Did you hope it contained an excuse for you and your sister?

*You must avoid faults in future; when you try to make up for them, you make them worse.* This is exactly the reproach I was expecting, and I can't tell you how it pleased and touched me. May I be allowed to ask who this fair lady is who is so interested in me and who interests me so little that I can't think even who you mean? There is another one however, and she has followed me all the way here. I don't need to tell you her name. Your mother was talking about her at dinner yesterday and she seemed to be watching me. And indeed I believe I looked and sounded rather embarrassed. I cannot tell half the truth; with me it has to be all or nothing.

*He says sweet, loving things to me, he feels them and believes them, but am I the only one he says them to?* What a chance to tell lies! But why ask questions like that? I have a mind to answer you in your own flippant tone, but it is beyond me. No, mademoiselle, I love no one but you, I shall never love anyone but you, and I shall always be conscience-stricken if I let any other woman think I find her attractive. And now perhaps you will say that that last sentence suits the guilty as well as the innocent. Your remark about the precautions of the wicked is unfair; and even if it were fair, how would it concern me? I have not been at all cautious, I let myself go quite openly and that is not the behaviour of a wicked man.

I am very glad that you and Madame Le Gendre and Mademoiselle Boileau are looking forward to seeing me, so long as you aren't counting on me to make peace between you. I am a dunce when it comes to falsehood and hypocrisy. But I do remember once reading on the table of a doctor of the Sorbonne these words: *Humility*, feeble virtue, *Hypocrisy*, vice which could be defended without too much difficulty.

You have seen all of them. You will see them again, I am sure you will. Goodbye, madam. Goodbye, mademoiselle. I too cannot finish without repeating once again the pledges I have so often made and which you have liked hearing as much as I have liked uttering them, because they are true and always will be. You do love me then? Remember all that has happened and make my reply for me.

My respects to Mademoiselle Boileau. Greet Madame Le Gendre as you like; I hardly dare say anything to her any more. I should either say too much or too little—as perhaps I am doing now.

## 6

*Paris, 12 October 1759*

I am in my friend's house and I am writing to the woman I love. Oh my dear Sophie, have you seen how happy you make me, do you know now how indissolubly I am bound to you? Can you doubt that my love will last as long as I live? I came into the company here full of the tenderness you had inspired in me; it was in everything I did, it shone in my eyes and gave warmth to my speech and energy to my movements. To the others I seemed extraordinary, inspired, godlike. Grimm was all eyes and ears for me; everyone was amazed and I too felt an inner satisfaction which I cannot express. It was as if a fire were blazing in the depths of my soul, I was all burning and the flames spread to the others and set them on fire. We spent the evening in a glow of enthusiasm which radiated from me.

It is sad to have to leave such a happy state. But there was nothing for it, I had to go and see d'Alembert as I had arranged. So I went and I spoke to him with the tongue of an angel. I will tell you about our conversation when I am at Le Grandval. Coming back from the Allée d'Argenson, where I failed to find you, I called in on Montamy,[1] who couldn't help saying when I left him: 'My dear sir, what a pleasure it has been to talk to you!'; and I replied under my breath to the cold man I had stirred up: 'It wasn't me, but her; she was acting through me.'

I left him at eight o'clock. Now I am at Grimm's; I am waiting for him to come in and while I wait I am telling you of the happy moments which we all owe to you. Here he is now. Goodbye, my Sophie; goodbye, my love. I am burning with desire to see you again and you are so near to me. Tomorrow at nine I shall be at the Baron's. Oh, if only I were with you, how much more I could show you my love! I am dying with passion and desire. Goodbye. Goodbye.

## 7

*Le Grandval, 17 October 1759*

This is the third time I have sent to Charenton, and still no word from you. Sophie, why have you not written? The servant went off the day before yesterday at half past two. I told him to leave any letters for me in my chest of drawers, which I left with the key in the lock. At six o'clock I thought he should be back. Time had never gone so slowly. I went upstairs. I opened the drawer —no letter. I came downstairs. I looked worried. Everyone noticed this, since my face always gives away my feelings. They talked. I took little part in the conversation. They invited me to play cards. I agreed. In the middle of the game I left them. I went to look, but still there was nothing there. I told myself: probably the wretched fellow has been enjoying himself drinking and will be very late coming home; all the better, I shall go up to bed early, I shall be alone, I shall go to bed and read the letter lying there with my head on my pillow. So I had a great pleasure to look forward to. I was impatient for supper to be served and eaten and for everyone to go upstairs. At last the moment came. I ran to the drawer. I was absolutely sure I would find what I was looking for and was very upset to see that I was wrong.

Why haven't you used the address I left you? Perhaps your

[1] Didier-François de Montamy (1703–65) was steward to the Duke of Orleans and an amateur chemist.

letters have gone astray? Or maybe you are paying me back for my silence and making me too experience the unhappiness you have suffered? Or could there be some other mysterious cause which I cannot even imagine? I don't know what to think. We are expecting a messenger from Paris here this evening. He will be coming by Charenton. He has been told to ask at the post office if there is anything for Le Grandval. He should be here at seven o'clock. It is four o'clock now. So I must be patient for another three hours and while I wait I will talk to my love as if I hadn't a care in the world, even though this is the opposite of the truth.

I wasted all of yesterday morning, or rather I put it to good use. I got a note asking me to go over to Sucy. It was from a poor devil who had dreamed up a financial scheme about which he wanted my opinion. It's an ingenious combination of a lottery and a system of shareholding. It is a pity he didn't propose it before the recent edicts. There is nothing reprehensible in the scheme. It could be introduced for a brief period or on a permanent basis. It would bring in a hundred and twenty million to the royal treasury. The rich would not be overtaxed and the poor would become the owners of negotiable deeds on which they could make a small profit.

They were rather surprised to see me all dressed and setting out so early in the morning. I have no doubt that the ladies discovered a romance behind my excursion. I came back in time for dinner. It was cold and windy enough to keep us indoors. I played three games of backgammon with the woman who once had beautiful eyes. After which Father Hoop, the Baron and I sat down round a great blazing log and began to philosophize about the pleasure and pain and good and evil in life. Our melancholy Scot doesn't value his life very highly. 'That', said Madame d'Aine, 'is why I gave you a room which looks directly out over the moat. But you don't seem very anxious to make the most of it.' The Baron added: 'But perhaps drowning doesn't appeal to you; if the water is too cold for you, Father Hoop, we can always fight a duel.' 'With pleasure, my good friend', said the Scot, 'but only on condition you kill me.'

Then we talked about a Monsieur de Saint-Germain who is a hundred and fifty or a hundred and sixty years old and who can rejuvenate himself when he finds he is growing old. We were saying that if he had a potion to make him one hour younger, by increasing the dose he could lose a year, ten years, and eventually find his way back to his mother's womb. 'If once I got there', said the Scot, 'I don't think I could be persuaded to come out again.'

This reminded me of a paradox which I remember one day trying out with your sister, so I said to Father Hoop ('Father' is the nickname we have given him because he is so wrinkled and dried-up and old-looking): 'You are in a sorry state, but if what I am thinking is at all true, things would be much worse for you.' 'The worst thing is to exist, and I exist.' 'The worst thing is not just to exist, but to exist for ever.' 'And I trust that that will not be my fate.' 'Who knows? Tell me, have you ever thought seriously what living means? Can you imagine a being ever passing from the state of not living to the state of living? A body may grow larger or smaller, it may be in motion or at rest, but if it does not have its own life, do you think that any change could ever give it life? Living is not like moving; it is something quite different. A body in motion strikes a body at rest and makes it move. But you can stop a lifeless body, set it in motion, add to it, take away from it, reorganize it, and in general arrange its parts as you like; if they are dead, no imaginable arrangement will give them life. To suppose that you can put one, two, or three dead particles alongside another dead particle and make a living organism out of them is an absurdity, if I know anything about such matters. What! Particle *a*, when situated on the left of particle *b*, was unconscious of its existence, insentient, inert, and dead, and simply by inverting their positions you could create a living, conscious, sentient being? It's impossible. What have right or left to do with it? Are there opposite sides in space? Even if there were, they could not be the cause of feeling and life. Anything which possesses these qualities has always possessed them and always will. Feeling and life are eternal. Whatever lives has always lived and will live for ever. The only difference I know between life and death is that now you live in the mass whereas in twenty years' time you will live in fragments, dispersed and scattered in molecules.' 'Twenty years is a long time!'

Then Madame d'Aine joined in: 'There is no birth and no death? What a crazy notion!' 'No, madam.' 'It may be impossible to die, but you can strike me dead on the spot, if you make me believe that.' 'Wait. Thisbe is alive, isn't she?' 'My little dog? Of course she is alive; she thinks and loves and reasons; she has a mind and she can use it.' 'Can you remember the time when she was no bigger than a rat?' 'Yes.' 'Could you tell me how she has grown so plump?' 'Why, by stuffing herself with food, like you and me.' 'Excellent; and was what she ate alive or dead?' 'What a question! Dead of course.' 'What! something dead put alongside something living began to live; can you make sense of that?' 'My goodness, I haven't much choice.' 'You might just as well say that if I put a dead man in your arms, he would come back to life.' 'Upon my soul, if he were really and truly dead. . . . But let me alone; or you'll make me say something silly.'

The rest of the evening was spent teasing me about my paradox. I was offered beautiful living pears and thinking grapes; but I said: 'Perhaps those who have loved one another in life and have themselves buried side by side are not as mad as we think. Perhaps their ashes come together, mingle, and unite. Who knows, perhaps they have not lost all feeling or all memory of their former state? Perhaps they still have the remains of warmth and life, which they can enjoy in their own way in the confines of their cold urn. In judging whether elements have life or not, we are guided by what we know of the life of large masses. Perhaps the two things are quite different. People think there is only one sort of polyp, but why shouldn't all of nature be like the polyp? When it is split into a hundred thousand fragments the original parent polyp no longer exists, but all its elements continue to live.'

Oh my Sophie, so I might still hope to touch you, to feel you, to love you, to approach you, to unite and mingle with you when we are gone! If only there were a law of affinity between the elements of which we are composed, if we were destined to become one single being, if in the course of centuries I were to become one with you, if the scattered molecules of your lover could live and move and search out your molecules dispersed through nature! Do not take this fancy away from me; it is dear to me, for it would give me the certainty of living eternally in you and with you. . . . But it is seven o'clock and the wretched messenger still hasn't arrived. I am extremely anxious. I shall definitely go to Charenton myself tomorrow unless a downpour stops me.

Madame d'Houdetot was here to dinner today. She came out from Paris. She is returning there and then going on to Épinay. That will make a good thirty-five miles. This English expedition[1] is terribly worrying to her; she is a very tender-hearted and sensitive woman. We were talking about the wind which kept up a low, steady moaning through the house. I said that I quite liked the noise because it made you feel the pleasure of being indoors and lulled you into pleasant daydreams. 'That is true', she replied, 'but I cannot hear it without thinking that it may be keeping the English out of the Channel, and that we may be taking advantage of it to sail out of harbour and send twenty-two thousand poor men to England, not one of whom will return alive.' I should tell you that one of these twenty-two thousand men is a certain Monsieur de Saint-Lambert, whom you have often heard me praising and who is following the Prince de Beauvau out of sheer gratitude. His loss would be a matter of deep regret to all of us and would cost her a great many tears.

It is nine o'clock. We have had a hand of piquet in the course of which, incidentally, I had an extraordinary run of luck: four aces, four kings, a run of six, repique, and finally capot. Then we had supper. Our messenger has arrived home. There were letters for everyone but me. Not a word from Grimm or Sophie. Surely you must have written. Either my servant must have lied to me and not gone as far as Charenton, or else the post-master would not hand over my letters to the messenger, or else he didn't have enough money to pay for them. I imagine all the possibilities which reassure me. I blame everything but you.

Our neighbour Monsieur de Sucy has heard from Lisbon that the King of Portugal has given the Jesuits the option of leaving their order, that fifty of them have accepted, that one hundred and fifty of them have been put on a boat for an unknown destination, and that four of them are still in prison and will be executed. But let Jesuits murder kings with impunity or not as they will, I don't care what becomes of them if only I have news of my love! Where is she now? What is she doing? If my letters are not as unlucky as hers, she will have received two together the day

[1] An episode in the Seven Years' War. The French fleet, commanded by the Maréchal de Conflans, did not leave harbour in Brest until the following month and was routed by the fleet of Admiral Hawke on 20 November 1759.

before yesterday. She will have this one tomorrow evening and perhaps . . . . but I dare no longer hope for anything.

My love, I came here to work. Until now I have got on quite well. But if I can no longer keep my mind on it, what do you expect me to do with the time? What will become of me? I only hope the rain which this noisy wind threatens us with falls tonight. Must I spend tomorrow without any word from you? The Baron comes to consult me about chemical etiology. He sees that I am preoccupied. He reads me passages from history and tries to distract me, but it's no good, my thoughts are far away. I beg you, my love, let me return to the country, my work, the company here, our pastimes, my friends and myself. I cannot leave here, but neither can I live here if you forget me.

Goodbye, cruel, silent Sophie. Goodbye.

## 8

*Le Grandval, 30 October 1759*

Here is the letter I promised you, my dear. Be patient and read it right through; perhaps you will find things in it which are to your liking.

Sunday was a very fine day; we went for a walk on the banks of the Marne. We followed the river from the bottom of our slopes here as far as Champigny. Champigny is set on the hilltop, like an amphitheatre. Down below, the winding bed of the Marne divides up to form a group of several little willow-covered islands. Its waters race smoothly through the narrow straits which separate them; at this point the peasants have set up their fishing-nets. It is a truly poetic spot, with Saint-Maur down in the valley on one side, Chennevières and Champigny on the other side perched on the hills, and in between them the Marne with its vineyards, woods, and meadows. The imagination would be hard put to it to bring together greater richness and variety than Nature displays there. We have made plans to go that way again, even though we returned from our walk in a sorry state. I had got a thorn in my finger, the Baron had a stiff neck, and our melancholy Scot had the beginnings of a bilious attack.

It was time for us to be back in the drawing room. Imagine us all there: the women are reclining in the background, the men all gathered round the fire, the former resting while the latter warm themselves. Everyone is silent for the time being, but it will not last. The silence is broken by Madame d'Holbach saying: 'Mother, why don't we have a game of cards?' 'No, I'd rather rest and talk.' 'As you like. Let us rest and talk. . . .' I don't need to name all the speakers in what follows, you know them all.[1]

'Well philosopher, how is your work progressing?'[2] 'I have reached the Arabs and the Saracens.' 'Mohammed, women's greatest friend?' 'Yes, and reason's greatest enemy.' 'That's an impertinent remark.' 'It's not a remark, madam, it's a fact.' 'There's another silly remark.' 'These gentlemen do talk in a gallant way.'

'These nations only discovered writing a short time before the Hegira.' 'The Hegira! What sort of a beast is that?' 'Madam, it is the great epoch of the Muslims.' 'That's a lot of help. I can't understand his epoch any more than his Hegira or his Hegira any more than his epoch. These people have a mania for talking Greek.'

'Before that epoch, they were crude idol-worshippers. Anyone to whom nature had given some degree of eloquence could lead them wherever he wanted. The men whom they honoured with the title of *chated* were shepherds, astrologers, musicians, poets, doctors, lawgivers, and priests, a combination you rarely find in one person except among barbarous and savage peoples.' 'That's true.' 'Among the Greeks Orpheus was such a man, among the Hebrews Moses, among the Romans Numa.'

'No news from Paris. My box-trees won't be planted this autumn. That Berlize[3] is a good-for-nothing. I need 150 plants and he sends me eighty.' 'Those beds will look splendid. What do you think of them?' 'Perfect.' 'I wish Charon[4] could see his garden now.'

1 The main ones are Baron d'Holbach, Diderot (the 'philosopher'), Father Hoop (the 'melancholy Scot'), Madame d'Aine, and Madame d'Holbach. See Introduction, pp. 6–7.

2 On the *Encyclopédie*; much of the matter of this conversation can be found in the article 'Sarrasins (Philosophie de)'.

3 Holbach's estate manager.

4 The previous owner of Le Grandval.

'The first lawgivers had the task of interpreting the will of the gods, appeasing them at times of public calamity, directing new undertakings, celebrating successes, allotting rewards, inflicting punishments, fixing days for work and rest, binding and absolving, calling together and dispersing, arming and disarming, stretching out their hands to relieve or to exterminate.' 'As people become civilized, these functions are separated. One man gives orders; another offers sacrifices; a third works cures; a fourth, more sacred than all the rest, makes them all immortal, and himself as well.'

'Madam, what they are saying is very fine.' 'A fine lot I care for what they are saying. I am thinking about my box-trees.' 'It's a long time since we saw Perfect Harmony.' 'So much the better.' 'They are at Saint-Maur, though.' 'Well, they can stay there.' 'That woman is more womanish than the whole race of women put together.' 'She never knows what she wants.' 'It's not so much that, but she's never content with what she has.' 'She seems more unfortunate than mad to me. There is nothing so tedious as desire, except perhaps possession.' 'But you must either possess or not possess.' 'It's a sad fate.'

'It was a man called Muramir who invented the Arabic alphabet and divided the nation into learned men, or those who could read, and half-wits.' 'The Holy Prophet couldn't read or write.' 'That accounts for the hatred of the first Muslims for knowledge of all kinds and the contempt for learning which has lasted right up to our time.' 'And for the long life of Mohammed's impostures.' 'It is commonly observed that religion's loss is philosophy's gain. You can draw all sorts of conclusions about the uselessness of the one and the truth of the other.'

'Your Madame de Charmoy promised to come and see us. What the devil is she doing in Paris?' 'Tearing her hair.' 'Why? She's clever and not bad-looking and everyone loves her.' 'And better still, she loves no one.' 'Mother, you are laughing at something.' 'I was thinking what her little man looks like.' 'Don't you think he looks like the neck of a bass viol? Just imagine a thing like that between his wife's legs.' 'That's the way, ladies, keep it up.' 'Good Heavens, son-in-law, allow us to slander our neighbours a little. I am sure they do the same for us, and it doesn't worry me. In fact, nothing worries me.' 'And anyhow, how can you forgive your neighbours their trespasses, if you don't know what they are?' 'Wife. . . .' 'What have you to answer to that?' 'That you ought to go and get your lute and play us a few tunes on it. The noise would be pleasanter and more innocent than this chatter.' 'Daughter, please do no such thing. I've never met anyone as miserable as your husband when he is ill.' 'It's like other people, when they are well.' 'You just keep to your philosophical babbling, can't you, and leave us alone. You were in the harem; go back there.' 'It's the quickest way.'

'Well, philosopher, so you were saying that the more thinkers there are in Constantinople, the fewer pilgrims will go to Mecca?' 'Yes.' 'I think he's right.' 'I'd go so far as to say that when there is an annual religious ceremony open to everyone in a capital city, it can be considered a fair guide to the spread of incredulity, the corruption of morals, and the decline of superstition in the nation.' 'What do you mean?' 'Look: let us suppose for instance that in 1700 there were thirty thousand pilgrims to Mecca, or thirty thousand communicants in one parish and that in 1750 there were only ten thousand pilgrims or ten thousand communicants, then it is certain that the faith, and all that goes with it, would have dereased by two thirds.'

'Mademoiselle Anselme.'[1] 'Yes, madam.' 'You have the ugliest bottom imaginable.' 'Really, mother-in-law, you are impossible!' 'Back to the harem, son-in-law! Yes, mademoiselle, a very ugly bottom.' 'I can't say it worries me; I never see it.' 'But it's all black and wrinkled and dry and little and crumpled-up and sad-looking. If Saint Peter knew about it, he would be less keen on having you.' 'And she has such a pretty face; how could she have an ugly bottom?' 'Just listen to our philosopher, who has me staring him in the face and still draws conclusions about the bottom from the face. In any case, hers is very ugly; you can believe me, I've seen it.' 'Seen it, madam?' 'Yes, seen it . . . all night, in my dreams.'

'Well, philosopher?' 'I've forgotten where I was.' 'Oh! take no notice of those crazy women.' 'Yes, but their talk about bottoms has gone to my head.' 'You had got to the annual religious ceremony and the decline of national superstition.' 'Ah, yes. I think there is a point where this decline stops. The spread of enlightenment is limited. It hardly touches the suburbs. The people who live there are too stupid, too poor, and too busy to

[1] Madame d'Aine's chambermaid.

be affected by it. It stops there. So the number who attend the great ceremony each year is equal to the number of those who in spite of the general revolution in men's minds remain blind or enlightened, incurable or incorruptible, as you prefer.' 'And that is what they call the flock of the faithful.' 'It may increase, but it will never grow smaller.' 'The rabble is always much the same in number.'

'Listen to what they are saying, madam.' 'I'm bored enough as it is. All I needed was the Socoplia. This seems to have been my year for ugly bottoms. Two months ago I was all alone here. I didn't know what to do with myself. I drove over to Bonneuil and tally-ho, along comes a man in a trap, as if the devil were after him. You know the turning off to the church? There was a woman there sitting on a donkey with a basket on either side of her, and suddenly bang! the hub of the trap catches in one of the baskets and there's the donkey with his hooves in the air on one side and the baskets and the woman with her hooves in the air on the other side. The people all gather round. They pick up the baskets and hoist up the donkey by the tail. But they left the poor woman screaming there as if she were being raped.' 'They don't always scream, you know.' 'Back to your harem.' 'It's the same there.'

'The Koran was the nation's only book for several centuries. The rest were burned, either because they were unnecessary, if they contained nothing that was not in the Koran, or because they were pernicious, if they contained something that was not in it.' 'That was the sort of argument that kept the baths of Alexandria heated for six months with the books of former ages.' 'Even after the impostor's death there were fanatics inspired by his ideas who damned the Caliph al Ma'mun for letting in learning to the detriment of the holy ignorance of the faithful believers. They said: If anyone dares to imitate him, let him be impaled and carried from tribe to tribe with a herald in front of him to proclaim: "Thus will perish the miscreants who prefer profane philosophy to holy tradition and reason to the miraculous Koran."' 'But what about the Omayyads?' 'They did little to help scholars.' 'And the Abbasids?' 'They were bolder. One of them set up pilgrimages, built temples, ordered public prayers, and showed himself so religious that he was able to bring to his court an astrologer and two Christian doctors without annoying the faithful.' 'There is no sect so hated by the Muslims as Christianity. Yet the learned men who were invited to the court of the last of the Abbasids were all Christians. The people did not object.' 'That is because they were happy under their rule. I should be inclined to say to a monarch . . . .' 'Can one say anything to a monarch? But go on, Father Hoop, tell us what you would say to him.' 'Be virtuous, be just, be victorious, be honoured by your subjects and feared by your neighbours.' 'Is that all?' 'I should add: Have a large army at your command and you will be able to establish universal toleration and destroy all those strongholds of ignorance, superstition, and sterility.' 'Will you be quiet! Don't you know I want to found a convent at Le Grandval?' 'What a marvellous idea!' 'What's more, you will reduce to the rank of ordinary citizens all those divinely instituted men who are constantly setting up their imaginary prerogatives against your authority; you will recover for your poor subjects all the wealth which the seditious wastrels are glutted with; you will double your revenues without increasing taxes; you will send their haughty leader back to the fishing net he started from; you will stop immense sums of money being swallowed up in a foreign pit from which they never return; you will have wealth and peace, you will be the ruler, and you will have achieved all this without causing so much as a murmur of discontent or spilling a single drop of blood.' 'My goodness, the tongue's a fine machine. Just listen how he trots it out!' 'But above all the monarch must always remember that the love of his people is the only sure foundation of his power. If he fears that his palace walls may fall outwards and looks for buttresses to prop them up, some of these buttresses will sooner or later push the walls in. A wise monarch keeps his dwelling separate from that of the gods. If the two are too close, the throne will interfere with the altar and the altar with the throne, and one day they will clash violently and destroy each other.' 'It would not be too difficult for a clever monarch to set the higher clergy against the Vatican, then to set the lower clergy against the higher, and so to bring the whole order into disrepute.' 'Just listen to them, planning how to drag the holy Church of God through the mud. Will you be quiet, you terrible atheists. Oh! and by the way, isn't Sucy's little devil-dodger supposed to be coming to supper? Well, if he does you'd better watch your tongue, son-in-law; how do you expect him to say mass when he has been laughing at all your filthy talk?' 'He doesn't have to say it.' 'It's not so easy for him to miss saying it as it is for you to go and hear it.' 'I have no doubt I shall do so one day.' 'Well, I do wish you would; he's such a good little chap, and he does like a joke.' 'All he would have to do would be to persuade the bishops that they could manage without the Pope and the priests that the bishops should share with them.' 'If that's the way of it, he looks like having a long wait.' 'Mademoiselle Anselme, come over here by me: if you don't want me to think of you with that ugly bottom I dreamed about, show us your real one.'

'The Muslims are divided into an incredible number of sects.' 'There are at least seventy-three of them.' 'They have their Jansenists, their Molinists, their Pyrrhonists, their sceptics, their deists, their Spinozists, their atheists.' 'The lucky people!' 'Just like us.' 'What a lovely brood!' 'They were all generated from the mixture of religion and philosophy. . . .' 'That philosophy ruins everything!' '. . . when they stopped proving the divinity of the Koran with the edge of the sword and started using their reason.' 'Reason's a bad thing too; I do without it as much as I can.' 'It shows sometimes.' 'Other people don't think so; but never mind.'

'They have their Manicheans and their Optimists. One day a Manichean said to an Optimist: A father had three children. . . .' 'Listen, ladies, a story.' 'One of the children lived in the fear of God.' 'Good for him. There aren't many of that sort around these days. I don't know what the world is coming to. The children are as wicked as the old people.' 'The second lived a life of crime, and the third died young. What will happen to them in the after-life? The Optimist replied that the first would be rewarded in heaven, the second punished in hell, and the third neither rewarded nor punished. But, replied the Manichean, if the third son says to God: "Lord, if you had willed it, I could have had a longer life and could have been sitting by my brother's side; that would have been better for me", what can the Lord reply? He will reply: "I saw that if I had given you a longer life, you would have been driven to crime, so that on the day of my Judgement you would have deserved to be punished by fire." But, went on the Manichean, can't you hear the second son objecting to the Lord: "Then why didn't you take away my life when I was a child? Why give me the miserable life which you refused my brother? Even if I weren't rejoicing in heaven with my elder brother, at least I should be sleeping in peace with my younger brother; that would have been as good for me as it is for him." How does the Lord get out of that one?' 'My goodness! I've no idea; that was a brain-twister for him. But we shall all know the answer when we get there; we all have to make the journey sooner or later.' 'He will say to him: "I prolonged your life to give you a chance to win eternal happiness, and yet you blame me for granting you this favour."' 'But then the third son will say: "If it was a favour, why didn't you grant it to me too?"' 'What a nuisance those three children were! They must have been a real cross for their parents; still, you must take the rough with the smooth. Let's go to supper.'

'Then there are those who reject any relation between the creator and the creature. According to them, God is just, because he is all-powerful. His attributes have nothing in common with ours, and we cannot tell by what standards he will judge us.' 'All the better for your friend Madame de Pressigny, Mother.' 'Let's leave her be. We must accept our neighbours for what they are. The daughter's as black as a gipsy, but d'Aine says she has white feet. What do I care if they are white or black? As for the mother, she would have done better to have looked after her eyes, which were perfectly sound, and let her husband be beaten up. But what's done is done.' 'They say: What is an ephemeral being who lives only for a moment, a single point in time, compared to an eternal and infinite being? What would the rest of mankind be to a man to whom God had merely given eternal life? Do you think he would have the slightest compunction in slaughtering everything that got in his way? Would he not say to his victims: "What are you, compared to me? In a moment you will have vanished as if you had never existed. You will no longer feel either pleasure or pain. But I have an eternity before me. What I owe to myself and to you must be measured according to what I am and what you are. Die then and do not complain. I am acting justly. . . ."' 'It's incredible the things that sprout in their heads. It's enough to drive me off my head.' 'And yet, how much greater is the distance between God and man than that between one man and another, whatever their attributes may be! Even if our man is immortal, what of it? He will still have a vast number of defects to bring him in line with our common lot. All notions of justice are obliterated between one man and another by the presence of just one divine attribute. yet we dare to imagine such a relationship between God and man!' 'Only the brahmin who is frightened of hurting an ant can say to God: "Lord, forgive me. If I have lifted up my ideas to you, I have also brought them down to the level of the ant. Treat me as I have treated the humblest of insects."'

'Among all these fanatics, there are those who make mock of everything.' 'That does not make them any happier or wiser.' 'Madame de Saint-Aubin, you have a chambermaid who is neither.' 'Why should I care?' 'My goodness, I should care in your place. I like to think that those who touch me have always got clean hands.' (This raises a sudden burst of laughter in every corner of the room.) 'What do you mean, clean hands?' 'Yes, madam, clean hands. I know what I have seen and I know what I know.'

'They have their intolerant people, like madam. . . .' 'Good Heavens! I don't get in the way of what I don't see. It's like Madame what's her name . . . come on, daughter, help me to remember her name.' 'Mother, you mustn't talk about that.' 'They came to stay here, I put them in adjoining rooms. . . .' 'Father Hoop, please go on.' 'An intolerant Muslim had attempted to kill a philosopher whose faith was suspect to him. This philosopher had powerful connections. He could have ruined the Muslim or had him punished; instead he simply reproached him gently and said: "Your principles tell you to take my life; mine tell me to make you a better man, if I can. Let me be your instructor; you can kill me afterwards, if you wish."' 'My word, what a pretty story!' 'What do you think he taught him?' 'His catechism; he didn't know it, even if he was a priest.' 'Arithmetic and geometry.' 'Perhaps that is what we should always do when there's a nation to convert: send in the mathematician before the missionary.' 'And why not the chemicist too with his curbitudes?' 'That might not be a bad idea either, Madam. Let them learn to put units together first, then they can be taught how to put together more difficult ideas.' 'Well, that's the most sensible thing you've said all evening. If your idea catches on, my lovesick Montamy will go off to Cochin China and stop boring me. Now let's go to supper and the devil take the little devil-dodger for keeping us waiting.'

And that's how time goes, my dear. All I have to write to you about is my love and our conversations. In the middle of this half-serious and half-comic talk, I sometimes sigh and say to myself: Oh, if only my Sophie and her sister were here! And then I sigh again.

Monsieur de Berlize left for Paris yesterday; he is taking you a letter. I went with him as far as Charenton, where I was hoping to collect a letter from you, and I was not disappointed. I arrived back here at seven o'clock. They were waiting for me to make up a game of piquet. I played cheerfully and won.

We are losing our Scotsman tomorrow. I shall miss him; he is a good man, sensible and very knowledgeable. His melancholia has taken him into all the corners of the earth and he has been giving me the benefit of his travels.

Madame d'Aine is the best of women, kindness personified, but she is always deforming words. She calls a chemist a chemicist, a cucurbit a curbitude, the Encyclopedia the Socoplia and so on. Perfect Harmony is a certain Madame de Back who took it into her head to found a female society under that name. Madame de Pressigny is the wife of a customs official at Bordeaux, whose life she saved in a riot. She threw herself into the midst of the rioters. They were so amazed at the sight of this dishevelled woman, wandering about exposed to the stones which were flying in all directions, that they stopped their rioting. She was in a critical state and lost her sight and since then her infamous husband and her repulsive daughter have joined forces to torment the poor woman. For years now they have been bringing bitter tears to her sightless eyes.

The little devil-dodger is Monsieur de Sucy's chaplain. He says mass on Sundays and the rest of the week he plays the fool. He had been with us on our walk and should have joined us for supper, but he did not come in until we had finished. We had gorged ourselves, particularly the women. When the little priest arrived, we were busy talking nonsense and fooling about. 'Ah! there you are, Abbé. You ought to know I don't like being left in the lurch.' 'Aren't you used to it by now, madam?' 'Certainly not.' Devil-dodger is no woman-hater; he would gladly do his duty by them. Madame de Saint-Aubin was sitting down with her elbows on the table; he went over and leant on the same table opposite her, for he is inclined to be familiar. Madame d'Aine, tempted by his convenient position and his broad rump, took a chair, put it behind him, said: 'Hold tight, Abbé', and with a jump there she was, sitting astride him with her legs dangling, kicking her heels into him, shouting and poking him to make him go, and he meanwhile whinnying, bucking, and stalling, his coat riding up on to his shoulders and the lady's petticoats being pushed up in front and behind, so that she was nearly riding bareback and her steed bareback too, and all of us laughing and the lady laughing and laughing and laughing still more and holding her sides with laughter and finally falling forward on the Abbé and shouting: 'Help! Help! I can't stop myself, it's coming; don't move, Abbé!' and the Abbé, who didn't know what was going on, not moving and being drenched with a flood of warm water which ran into his shoes by way of the waist of his breeches, and shouting out in his turn: 'Help! help! I'm drowning.' And all of us collapsed on the sofas choking with laughter. Meanwhile Madame d'Aine, who was still in the saddle, called to her chambermaid: 'Anselme, Anselme, pull me off this priest. Dear little Abbé, cheer up, you didn't miss a drop.'

The Abbé kept his temper, and good for him. Mademoiselle Anselme's face was a fine sight too. She is the personification of innocence, modesty, and timidity. She stood there with her eyes wide open, staring at an enormous puddle on the floor and saying in a shocked voice: 'But, madam. . . .' 'Yes, yes . . . it was me, it was the Abbé, it was both of us . . . I feel a lot better now. . . . Get me some shoes and stockings and a petticoat and some linen.'

Madame d'Aine is a decent woman. The little priest is not rich. Next morning she gave orders to buy him a new outfit. What do you think of that, ladies of the town? We crude inhabitants of Le Grandval, that is all we need to keep us amused for two days.

Yes, my dear, yes, I have had all your letters. My mind is at rest. I am as happy as it is possible to be when I am far from the one I love. I hope you continue to enjoy the *Essays on the Mind.*[1] Even though the author didn't win Grimm's approval,

[1] *De l'esprit* (1758); this work by the philosopher Helvétius was condemned along with the *Encyclopédie* in 1759.

he would be somewhat consoled by yours if he knew you. I can see you, you and your mother. I can hear from here the scattered words which occasionally break the silence of your retreat. You are wrong. Madame de Saint-Aubin is no longer interested in me. She has discovered, after thirty years, that the noise of backgammon gives her a headache, so we have stopped playing. I tell you everything that we do here, word for word; you will enjoy it, because it is your friend who is talking.

It is true that I was growing impatient waiting for Berlize. He was very solemn and mysterious about the part he had to play. He handed me Grimm's letter in front of the whole company, but waited until we were alone to give me yours. Just a brief moment and I shall be with you, and I shall bring you an innocent mouth, lips *ditto*, and eyes which have seen nothing for a whole month. How happy we shall be to meet again![1]

## 9

*Paris, 5 September 1760*

I don't know why it is, but there are still three or four of my letters on their way to you, whereas yours always reach me in twos. This makes me twice as pleased when I get them and twice as impatient while I am waiting. It looks as if I shall never really know how your journey was. You can tell me whatever you like about your health; I can't really believe you. Didn't you tell me that you still had a cold and were too hoarse to read aloud?

You can rely on Damilaville; he does everything properly. Carry on sending your letters by way of him. But is your Monsieur Gillet to be trusted? I haven't yet had the chance of telling Monsieur de Bucheley that he had been fooled by his colleagues, but I will soon. I am delighted that Monsieur Desmarets is not in such a bad way as I imagined. What I wanted to say to you about Monsieur de Saint-Gény is that he is seriously ill and that his friends, who are very attached to him,

[1] I have omitted several pages which appear to be a postscript (and are printed by some editors as a separate letter); they contain lengthy passages from the *Gulistan* of the Persian poet Sadi.

and his superiors, who think highly of him, are sad that they must soon lose such a good man. It is the good men who are taken and the wicked who are left, my dear. Look after yourself.

There is an 'if' in your letter which I don't understand. It comes after what you say about how your sister looked after you. Finish your sentence and don't hide anything from me.

It had been ages since I last saw either Madame d'Épinay or Grimm, but Grimm came in to see *Tancred*[1] and Madame d'Épinay to have a tooth pulled. Chance made me a spectator at the operation this morning and friendship took me to the play this afternoon. I shall tell you about it if I have time.

I cannot remember anything about Ovid's *Fasti* or the *Tristia* or the *Heroides*; as for his *Metamorphoses*, I have always liked them. They have fire, imagination, and passion and there are some things which are sublime. Take the quarrel of Ajax and Ulysses over Achilles' armour; Euripides, Sophocles, Homer, and Virgil could not have done better. Another beautiful passage is the one where Orpheus' head is borne along on the waters of the Hebrus with his tongue still attempting to utter the name of Eurydice and the waves striking the strings of his lyre and making a sort of tender harmony which is taken up by the river-banks and echoed through the forest. Will the time never come when I can devote myself entirely to my Sophie and these divine poets, dividing my time between loving you and reading them? A fine piece of eloquence, a beautiful flight of poetry, a look, a smile or a loving word from my Sophie, all of these enrapture me equally. Everything which bears the stamp of truth, greatness, strength, and integrity has the power to move and inspire me.

Now I will take up my journal where I left off in my last letter. I had come here and written to you. It was late. Damilaville invited me to supper. I accepted. I am a glutton. I ate a whole pie. I followed this up with three or four peaches. Then there was table wine, malaga, and a big cup of coffee. It was one in the morning when I came home. In bed, I was burning hot. I couldn't get a wink of sleep. I had the most thoroughgoing indigestion. I spent the next day drinking tea. The day after I felt well enough to go and see *Tancred*.

Here is what I thought of it: the whole thing is balanced on

[1] *Tancrède*, a tragedy by Voltaire.

a pin-point and cannot really work properly, but the faults in the plan are made up for by all the beautiful details in the execution. The first act is cold, but you can detect in it the beginnings of something very exciting. The second act is cold too. The third is one of the most beautiful things I have ever seen. It is a series of great emotional tableaux. There is one particular scene without words which wrings the spectator's heart; it is the one where Amenaida is being dragged to her death by the executioners and recognizes Tancred. She gives a piercing cry; her legs give way beneath her and she falls to the ground; she is carried to a stone where she sits down. You have to have seen it to imagine the effect of this scene, with forty characters on stage, Tancred, Argira, the knights, the people, Amenaida, and the executioners. In the fourth act nothing happens, but there are many beautiful passages. I don't know what to make of the fifth. It is long, terribly long, cold and contrived, depressing in fact, except for the final scene which is very beautiful. I don't know how the poet could bring himself to kill off Tancred and finish his play with an unhappy ending. In his place I should certainly have made everybody happy. Saurin[1] told me that then it would no longer have been a tragedy and Grimm replied: 'What of it?' It would certainly have been a better play, but it would have needed a much greater genius to write it.

Damilaville does not approve of running into the arms of death because the woman you love has been unfaithful. He asked me: 'If you were in love and your mistress deceived you, what would you do?' 'In the first place', I replied, 'I should find it difficult to believe. Once I was certain it was true, I think I should give up everything that pleased me, and go off to the depths of the country until I died or forgot the injury which had been done to me.' Nature has condemned us to suffer all manner of unhappiness, but has ordained that time should smooth it away, even against our wishes. Fortunately for the survival of the unfortunate human species, there is almost nothing which can withstand the consolation of time. It is this which sometimes makes me wish unashamedly for a violent disease to carry me off. I tell myself: it would be an end to my suffering, and after a few years (which is a long time to allow even for bitter grief) my friends would

[1] Bernard-Joseph Saurin (1706–81) was the author of many plays, including *Beverley*, an adaptation of George Lillo's *The London Merchant*.

find a sort of pleasure in remembering me, talking about me and mourning me.

I am enclosing the *Discourse on the Satire of the Philosophers*. It is attributed to Monsieur de Saint-Lambert. Everyone here is agreed in praising it as a work full of moderation. Voltaire read his *Tancred* to Grimm when Grimm was in Geneva and said to him apropos of the simple passages and tableau scenes: 'You see how I have profited by your friend's theories', as indeed he had.

I don't know whether I won't go for a few days to La Chevrette next week. They all want me to patch up *The Gamester*[1] and give it to the Comédie Française. That will keep me busy.

Goodbye, my dear. I love you with all my soul, and nothing can diminish this love. Indeed I sometimes think it can only grow stronger. When I am by your side, when I gaze at you, or when I am in your arms, I feel as if I had never loved you so much as at that moment, but this is an illusion. Remembered happiness cannot equal actual enjoyment. How can you compare the raptures of the past and the bliss of the present? When I see you I shall be able to answer that.

It is still only the fifth of September. How time drags! Goodbye.

## 10

*La Chevrette, 15 September 1760*

Yesterday was fair day at La Chevrette. I dislike crowds. I had decided to go into Paris for the day, but Grimm and Madame d'Épinay wouldn't let me go. When I see my friends with sad looks and long faces, my reluctance gives way and they can do what they want with me.

Already on Saturday evening the travelling salesmen had set up their booths in the avenue under great awnings hung between the trees. In the morning the local people had gathered there; you could hear the sound of violins; in the afternoon there were games, drinking, singing, and dancing; it was a motley crowd

[1] Diderot's adaptation of *The Gamester* by Edward Moore was never performed.

of young country girls all neatly dressed up and fine city ladies with rouge and beauty spots, reed canes in their hands, straw hats on their heads, and their squires on their arms. At ten o'clock the men of the house had got into a carriage and gone off into the fields. At midday Monsieur de Villeneuve arrived.[1]

We were all at that time in the gloomy and magnificent drawing room; at our various occupations, we made a very pretty picture.

By the window which looks on to the gardens, Grimm was being painted and Madame d'Épinay was leaning on the back of the painter's chair.

Someone was sitting on a stool lower down and drawing his profile in pencil. It is a charming profile. Any woman would be tempted to see if it is a good likeness.

Monsieur de Saint-Lambert was sitting in a corner reading the latest pamphlet which I sent you.

I was playing chess with Madame d'Houdetot.

Good old Madame d'Esclavelles, Madame d'Épinay's mother, was sitting surrounded by all the children and talking with them and their tutors.

Two sisters of the person who was painting my friend were doing embroidery, one in her hand, the other on a frame.

And a third was trying a piece by Scarlatti on the harpsichord.

Monsieur de Villeneuve made his bow to the lady of the house and came over and sat by me. We said a few words to one another. He and Madame d'Houdetot were already acquainted. Indeed a few rather sharp remarks gave me the impression that he had not behaved too well towards her.

Dinner time came, Madame d'Épinay was in the middle of the table on one side and Monsieur de Villeneuve on the other. They did all the honours and very agreeably too. We dined magnificently, gaily, and lengthily. Then there were ices. Oh my dears, what ices! You should have been there to taste them, you who like good ices.

After dinner we had a little music. The girl I mentioned, who has such a light and skilful touch on the harpsichord, astonished us all. The others were surprised by her unusual talent and I by the charms of her youth, her sweet manners, her modesty, her grace, and her innocence; it is no exaggeration to say that she

[1] He was the nephew of Monsieur de Salignac, Sophie's brother-in-law.

was Émilie at the age of fifteen. The applause she received brought a charming blush of embarrassment to her cheeks. She was persuaded to sing; and she sang a song which went roughly like this:

> I yield to the force of inclination,
> I can no more defend my heart.

But I'll swear she understood not a word of it. I was looking at her and thinking to myself that you would need to be more wicked than Satan to approach her with evil intent. I said to Monsieur de Villeneuve: 'Who would dare to change anything in a work where everything is perfect?' But Monsieur de Villeneuve and I do not share the same principles. When he encounters innocence, he rather likes to be its instructor. According to him it is a special kind of beauty.

He was sitting next to me. We spoke of you, your mother, and Madame Le Gendre. He told me that he had spent three months in your part of the country. 'Three months is more than enough time to fall head over heels in love with Madame Le Gendre.' 'True, but she is so reserved.' 'There is hardly any woman I know with more self-respect than her.' 'She is quite right. Madame Volland. . . .' 'Is an outstanding woman.' 'And the older daughter?' 'She is fiendishly intelligent.' 'She is very intelligent, but it is her openness that I like best in her. I would wager that she hasn't told a deliberate lie since she reached the age of reason.'

Our sportsmen arrived home at six o'clock. The violins were brought in and there was dancing until ten. Supper was over by midnight and by two o'clock everyone was in bed; so we got through the day without the tedium I had expected. Even so, if I had been in Paris, there would have been a letter from my love, which Damilaville would have given me and which as it is I am still waiting for—and this would have given me a thousand times more pleasure than I had at La Chevrette. I only hope someone will bring it to me today, or, if the worst comes to the worst, that Grimm, who is leaving today, will send it to me this evening.

Where are you now? At Châlons? Are you forgetting me in a whirl of festivities and in the arms of your sister? Madam, take care of her health and remember that pleasure too can be wearing. How much longer will you be staying in Châlons? If by some chance this letter failed to reach you there, what would become of it?

Well, have they seen one another? What did they say to each other? What did they decide? I asked you to apologize to him for my silence; I wonder if you remembered?

If a suitable occasion arises, take advantage of it and give my deepest respects to your mother. And remember me to Monsieur Le Gendre.

I asked Monsieur de Villeneuve for news of Monsieur de Salignac; he replied that he was extremely well and expected to see Madame de Salignac at the end of October. Speaking of Madame Berger I said to him: 'Really, these husbands are the most utter idiots. Fancy making that little woman pregnant when she has hardly a breath of life in her. A lover would never have done that to her.' He was watching me closely, but I remained unshakeably and stupidly serious. I am sure he misunderstood me and laughed at it.

The Baron was supposed to arrive yesterday evening from Paris and he may well be with us for dinner today. If he stays until Wednesday, I shall go back with him and we'll go straight through the city without stopping. In any case I have made arrangements for your letters to reach me without a hitch at Le Grandval if you continue to address them to Damilaville.

I have seen all the d'Épinay family. They have their individual features, but they all have some excellent qualities in common. Monsieur d'Épinay is the soul of friendliness. It will be a sad day for Grimm and his lady when they are separated from him.

As for me, I can no longer distinguish different places and times, circumstances and people. Your absence puts them all on the same level. I carry about with me a weight which oppresses my heart and which sometimes suffocates me. Oh my love, if you had to suffer even the half of my unhappiness, you would not be able to stand it. Only your return will bring me relief, but when will that be?

When Daphnis first saw Chloe again after they had been separated by a long and cruel winter, his eyes grew dim, his knees failed him, he staggered and would have fallen, had not Chloe stretched out her arms to support him. My love, if some spell suddenly brought us together, there are moments when I should die of happiness. I know that no good form or respectful behaviour could stop me from rushing into your arms. I should embrace you with all my might and should stay there, with my face against yours, until the beating returned to my heart and I had strength enough to step back and look at you. I should look at you for a long time before I could speak to you. I do not know how long it would be before my voice came back and I could take one of your hands and press it to my lips, my eyes and my heart. Just to imagine this moment and describe it to you makes my whole body tremble, so that I am near to fainting. Oh, dear love, how I love you, and how you will see my love when we are together again!

Are you not a cruel woman? If I were by your side, I think I should. . . .—Well, what would you do?—I ought to scold you, but I would kiss you. Imagine, my last letter (which is quite a packet too) is sitting in Châlons, countersigned by Courteilles, and this one would have gone there too, so you would have been two weeks without hearing from me if Grimm hadn't been detained here by the desire to hear our young musician play the harpsichord again. As a result, he was late leaving and I received your number 12 and got my letter back from him, so now it is on its way to Monsieur Gillet with a new envelope and address. Please don't make any more mistakes like that.

Well, have you nothing to say about the *Discourse on the Satire of the Philosophers*, or about the tragedy of *Tancred?*

Goodnight, my dear, goodnight.

11

*La Chevrette*, 17 *September* 1760

I am writing to you in haste. One of our painters is going back to Paris in a quarter of an hour and this note has to go with him to the Hôtel de Clermont-Tonnerre. I am enclosing a piece of nonsense with it. I ask no more about the arrangement which the philosopher and our dear sister have come to. I had laid out all your letters on my desk; I was intending to catch up with anything I had forgotten to reply to, but for the last five or six days this house has been in such a whirl that it has been the middle of the night before I have had any time to myself.

I have just had a slight accident. I had gone for a walk round a lake where there are swans. These birds are so jealous of their territory that as soon as you go near them they come flying at you. I was amusing myself by putting them through their paces; when they had flown to one end of their domain, I would suddenly appear at the other. To do this I had to run as fast as I could. I was in full flight, when I hit my foot against a metal bar used to open the covers of the holes which you find round these artificial ponds and which they call *regards*. The impact was so violent that the corner of the bar all but cut my shoe buckle in two; my instep was cut and covered with bruises. This did not stop me joking about my fall, which forces me stay indoors in slippers with my leg up on a stool.

They took advantage of this moment of confinement and immobility to have me painted. It is an excellent portrait.[1] I am bareheaded, sitting in an armchair wearing a dressing-gown; my left arm is resting on my right and is propping up my head, my collar is undone and my eyes are looking meditatively into the distance. And indeed I am really meditating in this picture. I am alive, breathing, animated; you can see thought behind the forehead. There is a painting of Madame d'Épinay to match; you will have no difficulty in guessing who the two portraits are meant for. She is leaning on a table, with one arm nonchalantly resting on the other and her head slightly turned as if she were looking to one side; her long black hair is gathered up in a ribbon round her forehead, but a few locks have slipped out from under this ribbon, some of them on to her bosom. The rest is spread over her shoulders and brings out the whiteness of her skin. Her dress is simple and casual.

I was intending to go back to Paris this evening, but my accident and these portraits will keep me here until Sunday. On Sunday we shall all be leaving. Grimm is going to Versailles on Tuesday and Madame d'Épinay to Le Grandval on Monday. I shall be staying in Paris.

I arrived at La Chevrette just as Saurin was leaving to go and visit Monsieur de Trudaine at Montigny. We have had two or

[1] An engraving of this portrait is reproduced as the frontispiece to this volume.

three charming letters from him, half in verse and half in prose. There is one of them, the latest, where under cover of advice to me on the danger of looking too closely at big black eyes, he in fact makes a very subtle declaration of love to Madame d'Épinay. This worried her a little at first. Her worry was the subject of one of our conversations in which, among various excellent remarks, she made one which I should like you to pass on to your sister. I was telling her, as your sister told me one day at the Palais-Royal when I advised her to rebuff straight away any man with whom she did not wish to become involved, that you risked seeming ridiculous if you rejected advances which it could be claimed, rightly or wrongly, had never been made; and she replied that it was better to run that risk than to compromise a decent man's happiness. There's a complicated sentence for you, but you will know what I mean.

Goodbye, my dear. I embrace you with all my heart. My most tender feelings to you and my most respectful feelings to Madame Le Gendre.

* * *

I am continually being interrupted and I don't know what I am writing. I shall take every opportunity of sending you my news. In one of my letters which you have not received yet I asked you the meaning of a certain 'if' followed by dots; please tell me at the same time what prevented your trip to Châlons. I see by the piece of nonsense that Madame Le Gendre is with you, or very soon will be. I have grown so touchy and unreasonable and jealous; you say such nice things about her and are so impatient if anyone finds fault with her that . . . I dare not finish my sentence! I am ashamed of my feelings, but cannot prevent them. Your mother says that your sister likes pretty women and it is certain that she is very affectionate towards you; then think of that nun she was so fond of, and the voluptuous and loving way she sometimes has of leaning over you, and her fingers so curiously intertwined with yours!

Goodbye. I am insane; would you have me otherwise? Goodbye. How much longer shall I have to keep saying that gloomy word, goodbye?[1]

[1] The last two paragraphs are a postscript.

## 12

*La Chevrette, 30 September 1760*

Really, my dear, your Desmarets[1] was good for nothing. You couldn't make either an honest man or a scoundrel out of him. If he is not already completely dull, it will not be long until he is. In fact, you only have to cast an eye over men's contradictions and vacillations to realize that most of them are born half stupid and half mad. Characterless, faceless creatures, they cannot choose either vice or virtue. They are incapable of sacrificing either themselves or other people; and whether they act well or badly, they are unhappy, and I pity them.

These ideas are connected with others which I was expounding yesterday at the dinner table—rather unwisely, as it was strong meat for our feeble stomachs. What I was saying is that I could not help admiring human nature, even in its moments of atrocity. For example, I said, a man was condemned to death for putting up seditious placards and the day after his execution even more violent ones were found on the street corners. Even at the execution of a thief there are thieves at work in the crowd, risking the very same fate they see before them. What contempt of death and of life! If the wicked did not show this energy in the cause of evil, the virtuous would not show it in the cause of good. If debilitated man has lost the strength to commit great crimes, he will have no strength for great acts of virtue. In seeking to improve him in one way, you will degrade him in others. If Tarquin no longer dares to violate Lucretia, Scaevola will not hold his wrist over the burning coals. It is a curious thought: we are usually dissatisfied enough with the way things are, but we could not touch them without making them worse.

In the course of this conversation about human nature we raised the question of how it is that fools always succeed and sensible people always fail, as if the first had been predestined to good luck from the beginning of time and the second to misfortune. I replied that life was a game of chance, that the fools did not carry on playing long enough to reap the fruits of their folly or the sensible people the fruits of their good sense. They

[1] A government official at Vitry-le-François, who had delivered many of Diderot's letters to Sophie.

quit the game just when their luck is about to turn, so that in my system a lucky fool and an unfortunate man of sense are two beings who have not lived long enough. And that is how the talk goes here.

So you have received two of my letters at the same time—and I two of yours. Only a flight of the imagination, you say, or a thoughtless flash of wit? Very well, but malicious people who wanted to ruin our happiness would not proceed otherwise. That is how they would find a way to estrange my Sophie from me and make her mother hate her. What sort of delicacy is there in such behaviour? Delicacy is a meaningless word if it does not entail foreseeing what little things are capable of offending, wounding, hurting, humiliating, or compromising other people, and doing your friends, without their being aware of it, the small acts of kindness which they have no right to expect from those who are not their friends and which they could not hope to receive from the clumsy and hearty benevolence of those obtuse people who are incapable of delicacy.

I want you and your sister to know that I am constantly comparing you with the idea I have formed of your minds and characters, and this is no ordinary standard of comparison. Set against it, most other people would look small indeed. I shall scold you severely for the little faults which I should not deign to notice in the herd, and I should feel hurt if you were not equally strict with me. I want you to expect of me all you would expect of God, if he had my goodness or I had his power, and I want you to be surprised whenever I fail to live up to your expectations. If sometimes I am a touchy and difficult person to have for a lover, it is because I feel so passionately for you; if I am so ready to be cross with her, it is because no one in the world thinks so highly of her as I do. Oh women! if ever I let you do and say what you like, it will be a sign that my feelings for you are dead. I love those who scold me and I like to scold those whom I love; when I stop scolding, it means I have stopped loving. Of all those who are near and dear to me, I am the one I rebuke most severely and most often; and the reason why I put myself first is that, all things considered, I am even more anxious to improve myself than to improve others.

Still, I am glad you did not recognize her in the picture I painted of her. You see that I am replying to your second letter now. It must be because anger guided my brush and exaggerated her features. That reminds me of a funny remark the painter Greuze made about Madame Geoffrin,[1] who for some reason or other had upset him. 'By God', he said, 'if she annoys me, she had better watch out; I shall paint her.' I should say the opposite: 'By God, if she annoys me again, I shall stop painting her.' You can say what you like in defence of her behaviour with the excellent Marzon and honest Vialet.[2] I appeal to her heart, which knows more about it than you do. Why do I include myself in her harangue? Why, because she is speaking against men in general, and I am a man, and you must admit that on first reading it you did not think of any individual exceptions. It was only after thinking about it that in the interests of justice you were forced to go back on what you had said and ask for your friend to be excepted, thinking to yourself: 'Ah! dear sister, spare him. He is not one of them.' So there was a debate between the two of you, with her accusing me and passing judgement, while you defended me and appealed against the sentence. I was already condemned in fact and you were trying to clear me of a false image which she had invented and you had perhaps accepted. Whoever does an injury to the human race does an injury to me. Whoever says anything against friendship in general, tends to make me secretly discontented with my friends; whoever makes fun of the sincere vows of passion in the presence of my beloved, angers me because he casts doubt on the genuineness of my actions and feelings. But enough of that.

I am at La Chevrette at the moment. That is where I am writing from. Tomorrow I shall be back in Paris. There are too many people here for comfort. In crowds everyone has to mingle, so that friends are kept apart from one another by strangers.

Yesterday I was sitting next to Madame d'Houdetot at supper and she said: 'I got married so as to see society and go to balls, promenades, operas and plays; but I didn't see society and didn't go anywhere and got nothing for my pains.' As you can imagine, these 'pains' raised a laugh, so she added:' My neighbour is drinking all the wine, but I am the one who is getting drunk.'

[1] Madame Geoffrin (1699–1777) was well-known for her Wednesdays, at which she received many writers and philosophers.

[2] Two of Madame Le Gendre's unsuccessful suitors.

And indeed there was a delicious white wine near me which I did not despise.

There they go now, off hunting. Thank goodness! They will have their exercise, we shall have some time to ourselves and this will be all to the good for them and for us.

I have not seen Mademoiselle Boileau yet; but I was nearly carried off and brought here by Monsieur de Villeneuve in his carriage. Grimm, who had met him somewhere in Paris, had asked him to do so and he had agreed.

If Monsieur Gillet has not been too slow about it, you should have your box by now; I will pay what I owe you on your return. How I shall embrace you! The thought of it makes my heart beat faster and brings tears of joy to my eyes. Hardly a day passes without my imagining the day when we meet again. I cannot describe to you what I feel in these moments of delirium: I see you, I gaze at you to see if you have been well, if it is still you, still my Sophie, if she is happy to be once again with the man who loves her so tenderly and has waited so long for her. My eyes devour you, my lips tremble. I try to talk to you, but I cannot. And then imagine my feelings when the illusion vanishes and I remain alone.

I am sorry to hear of Clairet's illness; please tell her that I can never forget her as long as she remains devoted to you. I was not expecting to see Madame de Salignac so soon. Won't your mother be anxious to go and see her dear daughter? I am sure Madame Le Gendre has lost sleep over it. You don't let yourself be taken in by appearances like that. They were fighting in the dark, poor people; they didn't know what they were arguing about.

Paris tomorrow—or rather today, Monday. Tomorrow I shall pack. The day after, I go off to Le Grandval for six weeks. Madame d'Épinay is rather sad about this, and so am I. We had grown used to one another. We understood one another without saying a word. We exchanged looks of approval or disapproval. She will miss this wordless conversation.

Continue sending your letters to the Quai des Miramionnes; they will be forwarded to Charenton, where I shall have them collected as often as I can. You know that where I am, the masters no longer have any servants.

Monsieur Damilaville is a fine man who likes doing good and

does it with style. There are two or three good men and two or three good women in the world, and Providence has put them in my way. If I really deserve this gift, I shall value it fully for what it is worth, and if I value it fully, I shall no longer be inclined to grumble at Providence. I do not know what I could reply if she could speak and said to me: 'I have given you Grimm and Uranie as friends; I have given you Sophie as your beloved; I gave you Didier for a father and Angélique for a mother; you know what sort of people they were and what they did for you; what else can you ask?'

Yes, my love, I shall find everyone I left there still at Le Grandval, except for d'Alainville;[1] but I shan't do any of the things you imagine. I shall drink .I shall eat. I shall sleep. I shall philosophize every evening. I shall miss you every morning and often during the day. I shall sigh indiscreetly. Madame d'Holbach will notice and will laugh at me. Madame d'Aine will say that if I go on that way, she will have to take pity on me and have me drowned. I shan't write a word and I shall return to Paris on St. Martin's day, when I shall be mortally disappointed if I don't find you back in town. I am in fear and trembling lest your dear sister has the mad idea of going to Isle.

We still have our painters and musicians here.—And Jeanette?—Jeanette too, yes indeed. Alas! the poor child breaks my heart, particularly when she is happy and laughs. She has lost her mother, but still no one has told her. I am sure that if she looked at all the faces round her, she would guess from the sadness which her happiness causes that something bad had happened and was being kept from her. Is it not extraordinary though that we all feel the same thing and that her happiness makes every one of us sad? Oh my love! there are so many indications, so many subtle indications which can be seen by anyone who is experienced in the ways of the human heart. It is like a cave, all dark, and yet from time to time there are fleeting rays of light which reveal its secrets to others and to ourselves.

And the business with the swans?—Do not fear, I shall never go running after them again, and neither will our dear Abbé Galiani. He used to amuse himself by teasing them. They took against him and now whenever they see him in the distance,

[1] Henri-Louis d'Alainville was a court officer and a member of the *philosophe* circle.

they spread their wings and fly hard at him with their necks outstretched and their beaks open, uttering fierce cries. He dare not go anywhere near their pool. They nearly devoured Pouf. Pouf is a little dog belonging to Madame d'Épinay; there is no dog to match him for intelligence and friendliness. He is a prodigy for his age, so we do not give him long to live. Those swans look proud, stupid, and malicious, a very common combination.

I said that the trees in the park at Versailles were tall and thin and straight; 'like courtiers', added Abbé Galiani. The Abbé has an inexhaustible supply of droll stories and expressions. He is a treasure on rainy days. I said the other day to Madame d'Épinay that if Galianis were sold in the shops everyone would want to have one in their country place.

I wish you could have heard him telling the story of the *porco sacro*. There are some Benedictine monks in Naples who are permitted to keep a herd of pigs, in addition to their own community, at the public expense. These privileged pigs are called the 'sacred pigs' in honour of the holy people they belong to. Everyone is full of respect for them as they walk the streets. They go into houses. They are welcomed in. They are treated with great politeness. If a sow should happen to farrow in your house, you must surround her and her piglets with all possible care and attention. You are highly honoured to be present at the birth. Anyone who laid hands on a *porco sacro* would be guilty of sacrilege. Nevertheless one was killed by some not very devout soldiers. This murder caused a great scandal. The criminals, who were afraid of being found out, bought two church candles, lit them and placed them on either side of the *porco sacro*, which they covered over with a large sheet, putting a holy-water stoup and a sprinkler at its head and a crucifix at its feet. The men who were looking for the murderers found them kneeling down and praying around the deathbed. One of them handed the sprinkler to the officer. The officer sprinkled holy water, knelt down and said a prayer, then asked who the dead person was. They replied: 'One of our comrades, a good man. He is a sad loss to us. But that is the way of the world, the good men go first and the wicked are left behind.' But I haven't the courage to finish. You need to hear it told by the Abbé, not me. His stories are not much in themselves, but in his hands they become extraordinarily funny and audacious, an endless source of laughter and sometimes of moral lessons too.

It was he who brought me here. We are expecting Saurin, who has not arrived yet. This makes me fear that Madame Helvétius is in a very bad way. She came in from the country to Paris to have her baby, but she hasn't had the baby and has caught a putrid fever. She is a charming woman who has made herself free when most other women are slaves.

Saurin consulted me about a plan for a play.[1] I turned the whole thing on its head. Grimm and Madame d'Épinay say that my plan is marvellous, but that no one but I would be able to write a word of it. If he follows my advice, you will see in Act IV a crowd of townspeople, condemned to death for defending their town too well, competing for the honour of dying and drawing lots for it. You will see them drawing lots on stage. Imagine the scene and the cries of the fathers, mothers, relations, friends, and children as the fatal numbers appear. Imagine the different expressions, the firmness and the weakness of those who are condemned by fate. Imagine that the man who holds the helmet from which the numbers are drawn is the governor of the town, that six victims are needed and that when five have drawn their numbers, he condemns himself to death, saying 'The sixth one goes to me', and remains inflexible in his decision. Imagine the effect on his wife and daughter, who are present. Oh Voltaire! you who know the power of the tableau, you would not be able to resist that.

But apropos of Grimm, aren't you a bit surprised that I have written seven or eight pages with hardly a mention of him? The reason, my dear, is that he arranges his moves so well that he always leaves La Chevrette just as I am arriving. Indeed, if he were planning to make me fall in love with his mistress, this is exactly how he would have behaved. I am only joking of course. He is too good a man to have anything like that in mind, and in any case I am too good for him to succeed if he tried. What's more, he is so immersed in negotiations and papers that he's wellnigh invisible. He hardly has a minute to spare for friendship, and as for love, I don't know where he fits that in.

She and I spent some time walking together this morning. I had thought she looked worried yesterday evening. I asked her

[1] Saurin's play on the Siege of Calais was never written.

the cause of her worry, and when she mentioned some trifling matter, I said to her: 'You are both only too lucky still to notice such things after four years. What a close eye you keep on one another, just as you did at the very beginning! Oh my friends, try never to marry!'

After dinner, we went walking again, she and Grimm, Madame d'Houdetot and I. I should have told you that I had made the lady rather tipsy; my white wine was excellent, I hadn't been any too sparing in my use of it and I had made her very merry, since she was sitting next to me.

Madame d'Houdetot writes very pretty verse. She recited me some which I like a great deal. It is as simple and delicate as can be. I did not dare ask her for any, but if I can lay hands on a 'Hymn to the Breasts' which is sparkling with warmth and fire and voluptuous images, I will send it to you. Although she had the courage to show it to me, I didn't have the courage to ask her for a copy.

In the evening we let the ladies retire and went for a walk round the park, Grimm and I. We had not seen one another for a long time. We were very glad to be together again. I really am fond of him and I think he is as fond of me as ever. In the middle of all these pastimes I am beset by gloomy thoughts. I am accomplishing nothing, time goes by and you are far away.

I have just had a packet from Damilaville. I didn't know what was in it, it was so fat. I hoped to find something from you. Not a word, but in place of it, the two Remonstrances of the Aix Courts, which are very fine, but no substitute for you.

I am dying to get back to Paris. I cannot keep my feelings hidden, and Madame d'Épinay says it is impolite to be happy when you are leaving people. So I suppose it would be more polite to feel just the same but put on a sad appearance?

Is nothing decided yet about your return? Is your sister coming back with you? If I had been wise, I would have made that trip to the provinces which has been so much talked about. At least then I should have seen you in passing. I am afraid you may find me rather changed in character. They say I look like a man who is always looking for something he hasn't got. It's only what you would expect. When you were here, your presence kept me going. If ever I felt depressed I could go and see my love and forget about it. Why have you abandoned me?

Melancholy found my soul wide open and went in through the open door, and now I don't think she will be easy to dislodge. I don't really dislike her. . . . But what of it? I shall be sadder, or not so happy, say it how you will, but I shall love you as much as ever. My love will be of the brown shade which rather suits that feeling. My dear, everything in the world is subject to decay; everything, even you, everything except my passion for you. When I see you again, how I shall embrace you! how I shall treasure you! how I shall seek for the one I love! Oh! if only there were no one standing in our way! But we cannot count on that. I shall not finish this letter yet. We shall be leaving early in the morning. Grimm will put me down in the Rue de Fourcy. It is only a step from there to the Quai des Miramionnes. If I were to find a letter from you there, I should fill up the half page I have left, or rather which I should not have left, since I should have filled it up with saying that I did not want to say anything else, if they weren't calling me to go downstairs. I'll go and see what they want.

It is Saurin, who has just arrived. Goodbye, my dear. This evening, if it is not too late, we shall be able to chat a bit more, then I shall have to pack. I don't like to keep people waiting.

We had two supper guests who weren't really expected, both excellent people: Saurin and the vicar of La Chevrette. You know Saurin, I don't need to tell you anything about him. As for our good vicar, he is one of the most interesting people for miles around. There is no one whose passions are more vividly expressed in their features. He is perhaps the only man there is who has an expressive nose. He distributes praise and blame with his nose; with his nose he affirms and prophesies. Grimm says that the man who can read the vicar's nose has mastered a great work on ethics.

We talked about all sorts of things. Madame d'Houdetout asked me from the other end of the table how my bottle was doing. I replied that she ought to know better than me. It was agreed that I was rather a lucky man to be drinking good wine and making my neighbour drunk. Then we talked about the news. Someone said that the King of Portugal was introducing Jansenism into his kingdom. I did not like this. I said that, as religions go, a monarch did better to choose an amusing and cheerful one, rather than a gloomy and miserable one, that religious melancholia led to fanaticism and intolerance—and all the time Madame d'Épinay was giving me meaningful looks, and finally, when I had said my piece, I realized that I was offending her mother, Madame d'Esclavelles, who is a Jansenist to the tips of her wrinkled fingers.

Then we talked about love. The vicar, who is equally at home in any subject, said that although all rejected lovers threaten to die, hardly any of them keep their word, but that nevertheless he had known one who did. He was a young man of good family called Soulpse. He fell in love with a girl who was beautiful and virtuous, but penniless. What is more, she came from a family which was dishonoured; the father had been sent to the galleys for forgery. This young man, who could foresee the opposition he would meet with from his parents and see the justification for it, did everything he could to detach himself from the girl. But when he found that all his efforts were in vain, he plucked up the courage to confess to his parents; they were just going to heap reproaches on his head, when he stopped them and said: 'I know everything you are going to say to me. I am bound to recognize the justice of arguments which I myself would put before my son if I had one. But you must choose between my death and a disreputable marriage, for it is certain that if I cannot have the one I love, I shall die.' These words were treated as they deserved to be treated—the result does not affect the issue. The young man went into a decline, pined away day by day, and died. The vicar added: 'I was a witness to all this.' 'But, vicar', I said, 'what would you have done in the father's place?' 'Sir', replied the vicar, 'I cannot imagine myself in his place. The feelings of a father cannot be guessed at and there is no substitute for them.' 'True; but still, you would have made up your mind in accordance with your nature. Tell us what you would have decided.' 'Certainly. I should have called my son to me. I should have said to him: "Soulpse has been your name until now. Understand clearly that it is your name no longer. Call yourself what you like. Here is your portion. Go and marry whoever you like, live far enough away for me to hear nothing more of you, and may God bless you." ' 'As for me', said Madame d'Esclavelles, who was perhaps anxious to prevent her grandson from taking the vicar's words too seriously, 'if I had been the mother of that young fool, I should have done as his father did and let him die.' And there we were in a fierce argument, with noise enough to make the rafters ring; it went on a long time and would be going on still if the vicar hadn't stopped it by telling another story.

A young priest, who was dissatisfied with his calling, ran away to England, abjured his faith, got married according to the law of the land, and had children by his wife. After a while he became homesick. He returned to France with his wife and children. After another while, he began to feel remorse. He went back to his religion, had doubts about the validity of his marriage and wondered if he should leave his wife. He made a clean breast of it to our vicar, who found the case a very tricky one and, not feeling able to take the responsibility for it, referred him to the casuists and the lawyers. They all agreed that he would be endangering his conscience by continuing to live with his wife. His wife did all she could to prevent the separation, and it was just about to come to law when the husband fell ill, and so seriously ill that he was given up for lost. He sent for the vicar: 'My good friend', he said to him, 'you know what my intention was. Now that my last hour has come, I want at least to show that it was sincere. Before receiving the last rites I want to make a public confession and then to die in the poor-house. Be so kind as to have me taken there.' 'I shall do nothing of the kind', replied the vicar. 'This woman is guiltless. She married you according to the law. She knew nothing of the obstacles which might have prevented her from accepting your hand. And these children, how are they to blame for your crime? You are the only guilty one and they will be punished. Your wife will be dishonoured. Your children will be declared illegitimate. What becomes of justice in all this? They undoubtedly have reason on their side, and until the law has pronounced, we cannot tell whether it will be for them or against them. Until then, my friend, you must remain in the bed of the woman whom you have called your wife, the bed where she has borne you children who have called you their father and who are your children.' Nothing would make the vicar change his mind. He heard the man's confession and gave him the last sacraments. The man died and his wife and children remained in possession of their rights, and we all applauded the wise behaviour of the vicar. Grimm has had his portrait painted. He says that one day he will make a character in a novel out of him. We were rather late coming home; this curious man and his equally curious stories gave us something to talk about on the way.

Incidentially, I forgot to tell you that the Comte de Bissy had sent the Marquis de Chimène a play for me, an English tragedy in one act, very much in the style of *The Gamester*. It is called *The Fatal Extravagance*.[1] A man of good birth has been brought by wild living into a state of extreme poverty. He cannot bear to think of the degradation which awaits him, together with his wife and children. He decides that it is better for him to die. But if death is preferable to life for him, why should it not be better also for his wife and children? He manages to persuade himself that he would be acting most unworthily by them if he did not let them share in a fate which seems to him preferable to the one which threatens him. So he kills himself, his wife, and his two children.

This atrocious ending repels the reader, but the last scene is quite heart-rending. Imagine the man on the point of being arrested and thrown into prison. His wife comes to him and offers to take the children in her arms and escape with him to a safe place. All the last scene hangs on the double meaning of words such as *journey*, *refuge*, *peaceful dwelling*, *far from mankind*, *the end of suffering and tribulation*, and *rest*, all of which can be applied equally to a real escape and to death. The ignorance of this woman, who has been given the fatal potion by her husband and has given it with her own hand to her two children, her loving words, and the presence of her children with death already running through their veins, all this is a thousand times more horrifying than the sight of Oedipus with his eyes put out bending down to feel for his children. Even so, if you have a copy of Father Brumoy's translation, look at this scene in the fifth act of Sophocles' *Oedipus*.

I have just had your number 21. My head is in quite good shape. As for my foot, it is quite better. We have been playing cards. The Baron forgot his good resolution, but since Fortune did not favour anyone in particular, I do not know how he would have reacted to her whims. My fall must have had some side-effects. The first two days I felt dazed. On the following days, I had a spasmodic pain in my other side, and since then I feel as

[1] A tragedy in one act by Aaron Hill (1685–1750).

if I needed to blow my nose, or as if there were something stuck high up in my nose and trying to get out. I have been advised to try sal ammoniac. But I am drinking, eating, and sleeping and I don't feel hot or feverish, so I shall be all right.

Oh woman, will you always remain a woman in some little way? Will the flaw which nature made in you never heal up altogether? I could not help laughing at all the excitement caused by a trinket. I know quite well what you would answer. But I also know how it is possible to deceive oneself. I too wish you and your sister could take part in our conversations. Apropos of the Chinese, did you know that in their country honour goes back in time, not forwards. It is the children who ennoble their ancestors and not the other way about. And an excellent idea it is too, believe me. We surpass these people in poetry, philosophy and geometry. But they are our superiors when it comes to the science of happiness and virtue, and if by chance this should be the most important of all the sciences, they would be entitled to say that they have two eyes, we have one, and the rest of the world is blind.

Yes, I know the *Interests of France Mistaken*[1] which you mention. It is a book which did quite well. Gaschon once invited me to dinner with the author. He analyses the illness well enough, but he has no idea when it comes to curing it. His observations are often correct, and show that he is an educated man, but no genius. He has a whole world of facts and can make nothing of them, whereas a genius can make a whole world of nothing.

No, no, he is a better man than I am. There is no one to compare with him, either in jesting, or reasoning, or giving advice, or writing or. . . .[2]

## 13

*Le Grandval, 12 October 1760*

Why no word from you? Ah! my love, our dear sister is with you and you are forgetting me, neglecting me!

[1] *Les Intérêts de la France mal entendus* by Ange Goudar (1720–91), an economist from Montpellier.

[2] The end of this letter is missing. The reference here is probably to Grimm.

I set out for Le Grandval on Thursday afternoon. I was quite right in thinking they had given me up and started slandering me. They were all the more pleased to see me.

'Ah! there you are, philosopher. I am delighted. Come and let me kiss you. I am not as young as I was, but I am healthy and I don't always smell nice.' This last remark was very wicked. As you will guess, it was Madame d'Aine talking.

The Baron and Father Hoop came down and embraced me. At first everyone talked at once, as you often do when you have not seen one another for some time and are very pleased to meet again and anxious to show it.

Madame d'Holbach was at her embroidery. I went up to her. She really looked beautiful. What a lovely complexion! What a glow of health! And how well she was dressed! Her hair was loose and she was wearing a dress of red taffeta, covered all over with a white gauze, through which you caught an occasional glimpse of pink. . . . 'You have just been at La Chevrette, haven't you?'—'Yes, madam.' 'Did you enjoy yourself there?' 'Yes, madam, quite well.' 'And so you stayed a long time?' 'Grimm and Madame d'Épinay persuaded me to stay for one more day, then another and another until it was a whole week.' 'While you were keeping us waiting, mama told some good stories about you.' 'Very likely, madam; but they are nothing but stories.' 'Why so?' 'Because they can be nothing else.' 'I don't see why.' 'Don't you see that there are some things in this world that are sacred?' 'Indeed, yes,' she said, looking down and smiling wickedly, 'and things that it is better not to come too close to.' That is the sort of thing which Monsieur Le Roy has taught her. Do you see what this one means? The rest of that evening was spent settling me in, and yesterday morning drinking tea and arranging my workshop, for I have brought a lot of work with me, even though I know quite well that I shall probably not do a thing. The Baron and young d'Aine went off to Grosbois to dine with the ex-minister Chauvelin. We were very merry in their absence.

There was a lot of rain on Friday night and a lot more on Saturday morning. The ground was soft and our ladies preferred staying indoors to the risk of losing their shoes in the mud and coming home barefoot. So Father Hoop and I went walking by ourselves, from half past three until six o'clock. I like him more and more. We talked politics. I had scores of questions to ask him about the British Parliament. It is a body with some five hundred members. Its sessions are held in an immense building; until six or seven years ago it was open to all and the most important matters of state were debated before the eyes of the assembled nation, seated in great galleries above the heads of their representatives. Can you imagine, my dear, that in front of a whole nation, any man would dare to propose a harmful course of action, to oppose a useful plan and thus make a public display of his knavery or stupidity? Naturally you will ask why debates are no longer open to the public. 'The reason', replied Father Hoop (for I put the same question to him), 'is that there are so many matters in which success depends on secrecy and secrecy was impossible. There are men', he went on, 'who have invented an abbreviated form of writing, so that their pen can keep pace with the most voluble speaker. The speeches made in Parliament were reproduced word for word as they had been spoken, both in England and abroad. This was a great drawback.'

Politics and morals go hand in hand and lead to all sorts of interesting questions and endless discussions.

Talking of happiness in life, I asked him what was the thing he valued most in the world. He thought for a moment and said: 'The thing which I have never had, health.'

'And what has given you the greatest pleasure?' 'I know the answer to that one, but first I must tell you something about my family. I have a brother and three sisters. In Scotland, as in some parts of France, the absurdity of the law puts everything into the hands of the firstborn. My older brother was the apple of my parents' eye; in other words they did all they could to spoil him—and were only too successful. They married him off as early and lucratively as possible. They gave away all they had to him. But their child, who was born bad and made worse by his upbringing, soon gave them cause to repent their folly in making him totally independent of them. He behaved disrespectfully towards them, treated them harshly, grew tired of them, wounded their feelings and in the end forced his good old father and mother to leave their own house, taking their daughters with them, and left them hardly the wherewithal to keep themselves, let alone provide a dowry for the girls, who were already of an age to be married. To make things worse, their brother had so contrived things that they were unable even to get their dowry from him. The unfortunate family decided to leave Edinburgh and go and hide their misery and their son's ingratitude in Carlisle. In the meantime my melancholy, which has carried me to every corner of the world, had brought me to Cartagena. It was there that I learnt of the unhappiness and poverty which had overcome my parents. I did my best to comfort them and reassure them about the present and the future. I sold what few possessions I had and sent them the proceeds. Then, seeing how quickly fortunes were being made all around me, I went in for trade. I did well. In less than seven years I was a rich man. I hastened back home. I set up my parents in their former comfort, punished my brother, married off my sisters, and I think this made me the happiest man alive.'

He seemed very moved at the end of his story.[1] 'But what did you do when you were a young man?' I asked him. 'I studied medicine', he replied. 'But why didn't you make a career of it?' 'Because it meant either remaining lost in the crowd or distinguishing myself by acting the charlatan.' 'It is very hard to give up a profession when you have made so many sacrifices for it.' 'It is far harder to crawl for a living, to have to choose between poverty and fraud.'

This led us to talk about the surest ways of making money. I said that in order to become somebody in due course, you had to be prepared to start as a nobody. This reminded me of what I had said to an ambitious young man who didn't know how to launch himself. 'Can you read?' I asked him. 'Yes.' 'And write?' 'Yes.' 'And count?' 'Yes.' 'And you want to be rich at any price?' 'More or less.' 'Well, my friend, go and take a job as lackey to a tax-farmer.'

That is how we talk, my dear. You were amused by it last year; why should you find it boring now?

After his studies, travel was what he had most enjoyed. He would gladly go on travelling even at his age. Personally, I do not approve of people going abroad except between the ages of eighteen and twenty-two. A young man should have the chance of seeing for himself that there are brave, talented, wise and hardworking people in every country in the world, and should rid himself of the prejudice that things are badly ordered in

[1] This story reappears almost unchanged in *Le Neveu de Rameau.*

every country but his own. Once he has done this, he should devote himself to his wife, his children, his compatriots, his friends, and all the ties which a man should feel most deeply about. These ties depend on living a settled life. A man who spent all his life travelling would be like a man constantly going to and fro between his cellar and his attic, his attic and his cellar, inspecting all the beauties of his house and never sitting down for a moment alongside those who lived with him.

That is more or less all we talked about on our walk, except for a scurrilous story which somehow managed to find its way into our conversation, in among all the serious subjects.

He was doing a course in midwifery with a famous man called Grégoire. This Grégoire believed in all seriousness that a child who died without having a few drops of cold water sprinkled on his head and certain words spoken over him would be in a bad way in the world to come. Consequently, whenever a birth was difficult, he baptized the child in its mother's womb—yes, in its mother's womb. Can you guess how he did it? First he pronounced the words: 'Child, I baptize you', then he filled his mouth with water, and blew it in the appropriate place as far as he could; then he would wipe his lips on a towel, saying: 'It only needs the hundred thousandth part of a drop to make an angel.'

The Baron and young d'Aine got home about the same time as us. We had our game of piquet. I have the impression that the Baron has learnt how to lose at cards. We had a good supper. A little more talk after supper, and then up to bed.

I didn't tell you that before leaving Paris I saw friend Gaschon. My goodness, how we talked of the mother and the two daughters! You would have loved to have heard us from behind the tapestry. Oh my love! always remain as frank as you are now, or even more so if that is possible, and you will win the confidence, the respect, and the admiration of everyone who meets you. If one day you should no longer be with them, how proud they ought to be to have known you! You would be the constant subject of their conversations; they would always speak of you with praise and regret, and they would add: 'Yes, of all these who had the good fortune to know her, the philosopher Diderot was the one she loved the best.'

I charged Gaschon to make my peace with Mademoiselle

Boileau, and he promised to use all his diplomacy. The Bouret affair is marking time. I greatly enjoyed hearing him cursing at all these people with their hypocritical language. He will not be going to Isle. He told me that he had made his excuses to your mother. So much for what I have done since I last heard from you. But why this silence? Does your sister take up every single moment which you manage to steal from your mother, so that you haven't one left to give me!

I don't know when you will get this letter, but I shall send it off all the same. This is what I have arranged with Damilaville. The day after he receives your letter he will send it on to one of his subordinates at Charenton. This subordinate will take back my reply and put it in the post at Charenton for Paris, addressed to Damilaville, who will readdress it to Monsieur Gillet. What a complicated business it is! If I were in Paris, I should be reading you already and replying to your letter; tomorrow my reply would be in the post, and in three days it would be with you.

Goodbye, my dear. If you do not receive my news as punctually as you might wish, do not think I am neglecting you. How could I better spend my time than in talking with you and opening my heart to you? Goodbye, goodbye.

## 14

*Le Grandval, 20 October 1760*

Here is the next instalment of my journal, my dear. I could perhaps have made a gay tale of it, but how can one jest and laugh when one's friends are sad? I am thinking of your mother, your sister, and you. How fortunate your friend is and how I envy him his character! Hope always stays down in the bottom of his box. With me it is just the opposite: if ever the lid of mine happens to be lifted, hope is the first thing to escape. It is not that I don't see the threads I could cling to, but they seem so thin and fragile to me that I would never dare trust myself to them. I would almost as soon let myself go with the current as clutch at a willow leaf.

We have had a lot of visitors here: there was Monsieur Le Roy, as I told you, friend Grimm and Abbé Galiani, Monsieur and Madame Rodier.[1] I love Monsieur Rodier's features. If only his mind lived up to half their promise! There is a combination of delicacy and voluptuousness about him. In the morning, when his long brown hair hangs down in careless curls on to his shoulders, you would take him for Hymen, but Hymen as he is the day after a wedding, pale and rather tired. Madame Rodier was dressed in a dark red colour which did not suit her and our Baron said to her: 'My dear sister, you do look lovely, just like an Easter egg!' Then there was d'Alainville and Madame Geoffrin, who was hardly bored at all, strange to relate. Then Madame de Charmoy with the same lovely eyes and interesting face, young d'Aine the monotonous, Monsieur and Madame Schistre (Monsieur with his lute and his dulcimer) and then two or three strangers to crown it all.

I like my comfort wherever I am, but particularly in the country. I have a woman's apartment here; it is the pleasantest one in the whole house. In the midst of all these visitors I still have it, and that makes me love our hostess a little more even than before.

The more people there are, the freer one is. My time is my own; never have I had so much leisure for reading, walking, being with you, loving you, and writing to you.

We had a merry dinner. Monsieur Le Roy was telling us how once he had been unhappy in love. 'Only once?' 'That is all.' When this happened he slept fifteen hours a night and grew visibly plumper. 'But an unhappy lover should pine away.' 'Or should give that impression, but I couldn't do it. That's what drove me to desperation.' His sleep was proportionate to his sorrow; and this made him ready again for sorrow proportionate to his sleep. 'Otherwise you would never have survived.' 'True. But after a night's rest I was all fresh and ready for sorrow. . . .' 'But if you sleep fifteen hours when you are unhappy, how long do you sleep when you are happy?' 'Hardly at all.' 'You don't find happiness tiring?' 'Not in the least, and in any case my strength comes back quickly.'

You can guess how this develops at the dinner table over dessert, with twelve to fifteen people there and champagne, gaiety, wit, and all the freedom of country life.

1 André-Julien Rodier, one of the Navy Commissioners, was related by marriage to the Holbach family.

Madame Geoffrin was in excellent form. I had a hand of piquet with her, d'Alainville, and the Baron. I am always impressed by her dignified and simple way of dressing. On this occasion she was wearing a simple material in a severe colour, wide sleeves, her linen very fine and plain, and everything spotlessly clean. She asked after my wife and daughter. I said I feared the girl would have an agitated and unhappy life, because she hates keeping still. 'All the better', she said, 'her agitation will make up for other people's laziness', and she took the opportunity of praising the cheerful and busy character of Madame d'Aine, who is kept with both feet in the air by her constant concern for our wellbeing, idlers that we are.

Ah my dear, where were you then? What were you doing at Isle, while I was wishing you here? Whenever I find pleasure, I wish for you. Imagine Monsieur Schistre taking up his lute. Now he plays. What music! What a musician! What a story his fingers pluck from the strings! It is unbelievable—and you may be sure Madame d'Holbach and I did not miss a word of it. 'Listen, he is angry!' 'What a sweet lament!' 'He is offended; but he is coming round.' 'I think so.' 'Now they are making it up.' 'That's right.' 'How could you resist a man who says he is sorry so beautifully!' And really, we both heard every word of it.

Monsieur Schistre put down his lute and all the others talked about their intense pleasure. We let them say whatever they wanted, preferring to enjoy the last of our emotion in silence. The moments of palpitation which come after great pleasures are very happy moments too, for the heart beats faster both before pleasure and after it.

Madame Geoffrin does not sleep away from home. At six in the evening she embraced us, got into her carriage with friend d'Alainville and away she went.

Around seven o'clock the others all sat down to cards and Monsieur Le Roy, Grimm, Abbé Galiani, and I to talk. This time I intend to show you what the Abbé is really like, because until now you may have thought of him as no more than a pleasant fellow with a naughty wit. There is more to him than that.

Grimm and Monsieur Le Roy were arguing about the merits of genius and method. Grimm hates method. According to him it is the pedantry of the literary man. Those who only know how to arrange things might as well save their energy; those who can only learn by way of a method might as well remain ignorant. 'But method helps us to see things clearly.' 'And spoils them.' 'Without it we could not turn anything to our advantage.' 'Except by exerting ourselves, and that would be all to the good. What is the point of so many people knowing things which do not concern them?' They said a lot more which I will leave out; indeed they would still be at it if Abbé Galiani hadn't interrupted them as follows:

'My friends, what you are saying reminds me of a fable. Let me tell it to you. It may be rather long, but you won't find it boring.

'One day, deep in the forest, a dispute arose between the nightingale and the cuckoo about singing. Each of them praised his own particular talent. "What bird", said the cuckoo, has a song as clear, simple, natural, and regular as mine?"

"What bird", said the nightingale, "has a song as sweet, varied, forceful, delicate, and passionate as mine?"

'The cuckoo: "I say few things, but they are solid and orderly and can be remembered."

'The nightingale: "I love to talk, but I am always original, never boring. I charm the forests; the cuckoo fills them with gloom. He is so bound by his mother's lessons that he dare not risk a note which he did not learn from her. But I know no master. Rules are a game to me. It is when I break them that I am most admired. How can you compare his tedious method with my delightful sallies?"

'The cuckoo tried several times to interrupt the nightingale, but nightingales sing all the time and never listen; this is rather a failing of theirs. Our hero was carried away by his ideas, darted after them and took no notice of what his rival answered.

'However, after arguing for a while, they agreed to appeal to the judgement of a third party.

'But how were they to find a third party sufficiently well-informed and impartial to act as judge? They looked everywhere.

'They were crossing a meadow, when they saw a donkey, the most serious and solemn of all his tribe. Never since the creation of the species had a donkey worn ears of such noble length. "Ah!" said the cuckoo when he saw them. "We are in luck. Our quarrel is a quarrel for the ear. Here is our judge. God made him especially for us."

'The donkey was grazing. Little did he think that one day he would be a judge of music. But providence amuses herself in many ways. Our two birds fly down to him, compliment him on his gravity and his good judgement, tell him the subject of their quarrel and humbly beg him to listen to them and decide between them.

'The donkey however, hardly turning his heavy head and not stopping grazing for a moment, makes a sign with his ears that he is hungry and that today is not judgement day. The birds insist. The donkey goes on grazing. As he eats, his appetite dies down. There are a few trees planted at the edge of the field. "All right", he says, "go over there. I will follow you. Then you can sing while I digest. I will listen to you and tell you what I think."

'Off go the birds, as fast as their wings will carry them, and perch on the trees. The donkey comes after them with the stately gait and countenance of a High Court judge making his way through the law courts. He arrives, lies down on the ground and says: "You may begin, the court is in session." There is no one but him in the court.

'The cuckoo says: "Your Worship, I shall not waste words; observe the nature of my song, and in particular be so good as to notice its artful and methodical composition." Then puffing himself up and beating time with his wings he sings: "Cuckoo, cuckoo, cucuckoo, cucuckoo, cuckoo, cucucuckoo." And after ringing all the possible changes on his song, he stops.

'And the nightingale launches straight into his song without any preamble, and tries out all manner of daring modulations and new and unusual melodies. His cadences and trills follow one another unceasingly. Now his song falls and murmurs deep in his throat like a rippling stream running over pebbles. Now it rises high, swells out gradually and fills the air as if it were hanging suspended there. By turns it is gentle, gay, brilliant, and touching, and at all times it speaks to the listener's emotion; but this sort of song is not to everyone's taste.

'Carried away by his enthusiasm he would be singing still, but the donkey, after yawning several times, stopped him and said: "I have no doubt that what you have been singing is all very beautiful, but I don't understand a word of it. It seems to me to be odd, confused, and disorderly. You may be cleverer than your opponent, but he is more methodical than you, and I am in favour of method."'

And the Abbé turned to Monsieur Le Roy, pointed to Grimm and said: 'He is the nightingale, you are the cuckoo and I am the donkey who judges in your favour. Goodnight to you.'

The Abbé tells good stories, but above all he is an excellent actor. He is quite irresistible. You would really have laughed to see him stretching out his neck and imitating the nightingale's little voice; puffing himself up and catching the cuckoo's raucous tone; and then sticking up his ears and assuming the stupid and ponderous gravity of the donkey—and all this naturally and effortlessly. He is a born mimic, every inch of him.

Monsieur Le Roy took the best course and laughed admiringly at the fable.

Talking of bird song, someone asked why according to the ancients the dying swan sang melodiously, when its usual call is harsh and nasal.

I replied that perhaps the swan was a symbol for man, who always speaks well on his death bed, and I added that if ever I had to make a poem of the last words of an orator, a poet or a statesman, I should call it 'The Song of the Swan'.

This gave a more serious twist to the conversation. We talked about the horror we all feel at the thought of annihilation.

'All of us?' exclaimed Father Hoop. 'Leave me out of it please. Once has been bad enough for me; I have no desire to start again. Even if I were offered eternal happiness in exchange for one day of purgatory, I should refuse. No longer to exist is best.'

This made me think, and it seemed to me that as long as my health lasted I should agree with Father Hoop, but that when the end came I might be ready to endure a thousand or ten thousand years of hell for the happiness of a second existence. Then we might be together again, my love! And I could love you again! I could persuade myself of what a girl once persuaded her dying father. The man in question was an old money-lender. A priest had sworn to him that he would be damned if he did not give back his ill-gotten gains. He decided to do it, called his daughter to his side and said to her: 'My child, you expected me to leave you a fortune and so I would have done. But this man here will be your ruin. He declares that I shall burn in hell if I die without making restitution.' 'You must be joking, father, to talk of damnation and restitution. I know you; by the time you have been in hell for ten years, you will be quite at home there.'

This seemed right to him and he died without making restitution. Well, if a daughter is willing to see her father damned and a father to be damned to make his daughter rich, how can a passionate lover and a good man be afraid at the prospect? Is it not sweet to exist and to be once again with your father, your mother, your beloved, your friend, your wife, your children, and all you have loved, even in hell?

And this set us off on a discussion of life and death and the world and its supposed creator.

Someone observed that whether there was a god or not, it was impossible to bring him into nature or a philosophical question without making things more obscure.

Someone else said that even if a hypothesis explained all the phenomena, it did not follow that it was true; for who is to say that the general order of things has only one cause? What then are we to think of a hypothesis which far from solving the one problem which it was invented for, gives rise to innumerable other problems?

I think you are always entertained by our fireside chatter, my dear, so I will go on.

Among these problems there is one which has been bandied around and never solved since the world began and men first suffered unjustly; it is the incompatibility of physical and moral evil with the nature of the eternal being.

This is how it goes: he is either impotent or malevolent; impotent, if he wanted to prevent evil and could not; malevolent, if he could prevent it and did not want to.

Even a child could understand that. And it is this which has made men dream up the fault of Adam, original sin, rewards and punishments in the world to come, incarnation, immortality, the two principles of the Manicheans, the Ormazd and Ahriman of the Persians, the emanations of the Gnostics, the kingdoms of light and darkness, reincarnation, metempsychosis, optimism, and all the other absurdities which are firmly believed in by the various nations of the earth, a collection of empty visions attempting to deal with a clear, simple, and evident fact.

What is a sensible man to think in these matters? He will

come to the same conclusion as we did, my dear. Whatever the optimists may tell us, we shall reply that if the world could not exist without creatures capable of feeling, and that if these creatures could not exist without pain, why bother to create it at all? After all, there was an eternity before this idiotic creation came into being.

Idiotic, the world? Even so, my dear, what a fine piece of idiocy! According to some people living in Malabar, it is one of the seventy-four comedies with which the Almighty entertains himself.

Leibnitz, the founder of optimism, and a great poet as well as a profound philosopher, writes somewhere that in a temple at Memphis there was a great pyramid of globes placed one on top of the other. A priest, who was asked by a traveller what this pyramid of globes represented, replied that these were all the possible worlds and that the most perfect of all was at the summit; the traveller, who was curious to have a closer look at this most perfect of all possible worlds, climbed to the top of the pyramid, where the first thing he saw was Tarquin raping Lucretia.

I do not know who it was who recalled this story, which I already knew—indeed I think I have told it to you before.

Conversations are peculiar things, especially when several people are involved. Just look at the roundabout ways we went. It is as strange a mixture as the dreams of a sick and delirious man. Nevertheless, just as there is nothing unconnected in the mind of a dreamer or a madman, so everything hangs together in a conversation, though it would sometimes be very hard to reconstruct all the tenuous links which join up so many disparate ideas. One man throws out a word detached from everything which comes before or after it in his mind; another does the same thing and we are launched into a labyrinth. A single physical attribute can bring an infinite variety of things to your mind. Take a colour, yellow for instance. Gold is yellow, silk is yellow, marigolds are yellow, bile is yellow, light is yellow, straw is yellow, and heaven knows how many other threads are attached to this yellow one! Madness, dreaming, and the disorder of conversation consist in going from one subject to another by way of a common attribute. The madman does not notice that he is changing subjects. He grasps a piece of shining yellow straw and shouts that he is holding the sun. What a lot of men are like this madman, unbeknown to themselves! Perhaps I am too, as I write this.

The word 'rape' linked Tarquin's crime to that of Lovelace. Lovelace is the hero of the novel *Clarissa*, so this gave us a leap from Roman history to English novels. There was a lot of argument about *Clarissa*. Those who had a low opinion of it had an extremely low opinion of it. Those who thought highly of it were as extreme in their admiration as the others in their contempt and considered it one of the great achievements of the human mind. I have a copy of it. I am very sorry you did not take it off to the country with you. I shall never be satisfied with you or with myself until I have made you appreciate the truth of *Pamela*, *Tom Jones*, *Clarissa* and *Grandison*.

So many wise and foolish things have been said and done here that I should never finish if I didn't break off to tell you about two comical incidents which I can't resist writing down, even though I know quite well that they are childish and not at all appropriate to your present state of mind.

Our rooms are all on the first floor, along the same corridor; some look out on to the front courtyard and the moats, the others on to the garden and the fields. Oh, what a gossip I am, my dear! As Madame de Sévigné said, for she was just as talkative and greedy as I am, 'Shall I never learn to stop eating and be quiet?'

It was evening and we had all gone up to our rooms. There had been a lot of talk about the fire at Monsieur de Bagueville's and suddenly in bed Madame d'Aine remembers that she left a huge log burning on the drawing room fire. Perhaps the fireguard hasn't been put up and the log will roll on to the wooden floor, as has already happened once before. She is seized by fear, and since she never orders anyone to do what she can do herself, she gets up, slips her bare feet into her slippers and comes out of her room dressed in a nightgown and bodice, and holding a little nightlight in her hand. As she is going downstairs she meets Monsieur Le Roy, who is on his way to bed after sitting up and reading in the drawing room. They catch sight of one another and Madame d'Aine dashes away; Monsieur Le Roy runs after her, catches up with her, grabs her round the waist, and begins to kiss her and kiss her, while she shouts and shouts:

'Help, help! Save me!' The ravisher's kisses prevent her from talking clearly, but you can hear something like: 'Save me, sons-in-law! If he gives me a child, you will be the losers.' We open our doors and come out into the corridor, but we find only Madame d'Aine in a state of great disorder, searching in the dark for her nightcap and slippers, for her lamp had fallen and gone out and our friend had retreated to his room.

I left them all in the corridor where they were still laughing at two in the morning, like those Homeric gods who laughed interminably—and sometimes with less reason, for you must admit that it is more entertaining to see a plump, dimpled, white-skinned woman almost naked in the arms of an impertinent and lecherous young man than to see a disagreeable cripple clumsily pouring out drink for his father and mother after a rather tedious family quarrel. This is at the end of Book I of the *Iliad*.

This adventure gave us something to laugh about today. Some people would have it that Madame d'Aine called out too soon, others that she only called out once she knew she was out of danger, and that she would have been just as happy to keep quiet and enjoy herself as to shout out and save her honour. And heaven knows what else they don't say!

The other tale is a first-rate piece of impertinence. You must imagine fourteen or fifteen of us at table, near the end of the meal, and young d'Aine sitting on the left of Madame de Charmoy. He is in the habit of being familiar with her. So he takes her hand, and wanting to see her arm, pulls up the sleeve. Whether deliberately or absent-mindedly, she does not stop him. He notices some long black hairs on her rather white skin and sets about plucking her arm. She tries to pull her hand away, he holds on tight; she tries to pull down her sleeve, he pulls it up again and goes on plucking. She cries out: 'Kindly stop it, sir.' He replies: 'No, madam; what use are they to you?' and goes on plucking. She gets angry: 'You are an insolent fellow.' He lets her get angry and plucks away undeterred. Madame d'Aine, suffocating and holding her sides with a mixture of laughter and anger, tries to adopt a serious tone and says to him: 'D'Aine, what are you thinking of?' and she laughs; 'whoever heard of plucking a woman at table?'—and she laughs; 'where is the education I gave you?'—and everyone else bursts out laughing.

There were tears running down my face and I thought I should die laughing.

However, a few moments later, the mother made a sign to her son and he went and knelt down at the lady's feet and begged her forgiveness. She claims that he hurt her, but that is not true. It was the unkind joke and our inhuman laughter which hurt her.

The Baron is ill. He has dysentery and a fever. I have just been down to the drawing room where he, Father Hoop, Madame d'Aine, and Madame d'Holbach were taking tea. I joined them. And in the middle of tea the Baron, who is as eccentric and disreputable as ever in spite of his colic, says: 'Do you know the Grand Lama, mama?' 'I don't know any lamas, grand or otherwise.' 'He is a priest in Tibet.' 'Wherever he lives, if he is a good priest, I respect him.' 'Once a year, after a good dinner he goes to his privy. . . .' 'Much good may it do him.' 'And there. . . .' 'Here comes some more filth.' 'Why do you call it filth, pray? It seems to me to be a need which is simple, natural, and more or less universal and one which you satisfy as well as the miller's wife, for all your spiritualism. But never mind, let's call it filth; well then, when the Grand Lama has done his filth, it is collected as it if were a sacred object, turned into powder and sent off in little packets to all the sovereign princes who take it in their tea on holy days.' 'How crazy!' 'Crazy or not, it is a fact. In any case, don't you think that if you were given one of Jesus Christ's turds, you would be very proud of it? And if a Jansenist were given one of the blessed deacon's turds, wouldn't it be preserved as a precious relic and start working miracles before long?'[1]

You had better not read that paragraph to Madame Le Gendre. She does not like that sort of talk. But I can say to you that this story of the Grand Lama is quite authentic and even though it may be rather unsavoury you can see in it one of the strongest proofs of the power of priests over men's minds.

Here is something for Madame Le Gendre now. Damilaville has sent me the *History of the Russian Empire*[2] and I have read it.

It is in three parts: a preface on the writing of history in

[1] 'The blessed deacon' is the Jansenist Diacre Pâris, whose tomb was the scene of many 'miracles' in Diderot's lifetime.

[2] *Histoire de Russie sous Pierre le Grand*, by Voltaire.

general; a description of Russia; and the history of the tsar from his birth to the defeat of Charles XII at Poltava.

The preface is childish. It is written in a facetious tone and is hardly worthy of appearing even in the *Literary Miscellany* of the same author. Near the end of it he argues that the historian should not write the private lives of great men. He backs up this strange paradox with reasons which seem quite plausible and respectable, but he is wrong, or my friend Plutarch is nothing but a fool.

In the first part there is only one remark I like; this is that if there had only ever been one battle, the names of all who fought in it would be known and their genealogies would go down to remotest posterity.

Can anything show more clearly than the evident truth of this notion how strange it is that men flock together to the same place to cut one another's throats?

If the animals who suffer so much at our hands could think about man as man thinks about them, would they not regard wars as a special dispensation of Providence and say to one another: 'If men did not have this insane urge, this thirst for one another's blood, which nature impels them to satisfy from time to time, their cursed race would cover the entire surface of the earth, and that would be the end of us.' If stags could think, what a great event the death of Louis XV would be for the stags of the Forest of Fontainebleau! What would they think of it?

And what about the fish in our moat? When we amuse ourselves by throwing bread to them after dinner, what do they think of this manna which falls from heaven in the autumn? Is there not among them some scaly Moses who takes the credit for our largesse?

However this may be, I have an urge to reconcile you a little to all the wars, plagues, and other scourges of the human race. Did you know that if every kingdom was as well governed as China, the most fertile country on earth, there would be three times as many men as there was food to feed them? For good or for evil, everything has to be as it is.

The description of Russia is hackneyed. It is liberally sprinkled with supposedly knowledgeable passages on natural history, concerning which the author is totally ignorant.

As for the history of the tsar, you can read it with pleasure, but if you ask yourself at the end of it: 'What great tableau have I been shown? What profound reflections have stayed in my mind? Which passages impressed me as sublime? Which pages do I want to re-read? Where are the signs of genius in all this?', you would find yourself unable to reply. I would rather have written this letter to my love. It will be buried between us. She will enjoy reading it as I have enjoyed writing it and this is all that is needed.

The French writer falls far short of the Russian lawgiver. Even so, if all gazettes were written as well as this, I would not want to miss a single one of them.

There is a rather fine chapter about the cruel acts of Princess Sophia. You cannot help being moved when you see the young Peter at the age of twelve or thirteen, clasping an image of the Virgin and being led by his weeping sisters to a horde of ferocious soldiers who are shouting for his blood and who have just cut off the head, feet, and hands of his brother. But what is that by comparison with certain passages in Tacitus, such as the consternation of the Romans when they hear of the death of Germanicus and the sorrow of the people when the ashes of this prince are brought to Rome?

In the description of the country there is a rather good piece on the manners of the Samoyeds. But I cannot stand this constant carping at works which are highly regarded. In two places he tries to belittle Monsieur de Buffon's *Natural History*. He picks on little geographical details and seasons his criticism with ironical eulogies.

And then, why inflict the Crommyonian sow and chaplain Norberg on me in a history of the tsar?[1]

Damilaville thought it was very good. I have scolded him for it, but I softened the blow by telling him as sincerely as I would tell you or sister Uranie: 'Don't be ashamed if I have to give you a lesson in literature or philosophy. Won't you always be proud of being my tutors in morality and particularly practical morality? You know what goodness is; you have a natural sense for it; you have feeling hearts and delicate minds; you are the real men and I am the grasshopper chirping away in the countryside.'

[1] The Crommyonian sow was one of the monsters killed by Theseus; chaplain Norberg was author of a life of Charles XII published in Stockholm in 1740.

But when, oh when, shall I see you? Will it be All Saints' or Saint Martin's day when business brings my beloved back to me and bad weather restores her philosopher to her? Philosophers must appear with the bad weather. It is their season.

I was in a mood to say tender things to you, since I must either begin or end my letters by saying I love you. If the parts of my letters where I talk about my love are the ones which Uranie most likes reading, they are also the ones which it is no effort to write and which I most like writing.

But now the bell is ringing for mass. Little devil-dodger has arrived. I can hear him laughing like a stag in October, to use Monsieur Le Roy's comparison. According to him you could easily confuse the two in a forest.

Half of our women will go and hear mass in the billiard room and half of them in my room, from which you can see the chapel door on the other side of the courtyard. According to them a mass is effective within a radius of fifty feet. We have no opinion on the subject.

I have had a word with Grimm about your business with Villeneuve.[1] He said that all those people were knaves, that Villeneuve was reckoned to have more than fifty thousand francs a year, that you must stand fast, that he is a coward and would never have the courage to be really despicable, and that even if he is not a very honourable man, he would be sufficiently attached to his public reputation to fear a scandal.

From which I conclude that you must diplomatically make the uncle see how unjust and contrary to the law his claim is and how he and his nephew would be blamed if it ever became public. You must keep it and not answer until it is in your hands again.

I shall reply to your number 27 and 28 by the next post.

It's a long time since you told me anything about your lump. Have you heard of hemlock pills? They are said to work wonders for all kinds of obstruction, wens, congested glands, cancerous tumours, etc.

I am growing as round as a ball. How you are going to loathe me, Madame Le Gendre! My stomach struggles against my waistcoat buttons and is furious that it cannot overcome them, especially after dinner.

[1] The young Vallet de Villeneuve, whose family had been ruined by the war with England, owed the Vollands a large sum of money.

Goodbye, my love. I am yours for ever in all things. It is particularly in unhappy circumstances that my heart tells me so.

We have no one left here. All the noise has died down. Now the Baron, Father Hoop, and I will be closer again. All those strangers who kept us apart have gone, thank goodness.

I shall post the letter you sent me for Monsieur de Prysie at the same time as this one.

Did you know, my dear, that you finished his letter with an equivocal sentence which would give a fop food for vanity and a jealous man matter for alarm? 'I should see all the pleasant company there, my sister and her children. And is that all? Oh no! I should never finish if I had to say everything.' That could easily be taken as coquetry, or even worse. But I don't know what you are talking about and Monsieur de Prysie will not read into it more than was meant. He is not a fop and I am not jealous.

Damilaville is an admirable man. Three times a week he sends a man here to bring me your letters and collect mine.

Goodbye, goodbye. Tell me well in advance when you are coming back to Paris, so that there aren't a dozen of my letters on their way to Isle when you are no longer there.

You are dearer to me than ever. Absence makes no difference. Yes, it does. It makes me impatient.

* * *

I have just read this letter over. I almost felt like burning it. I was afraid that reading it might tire you.

If you find it hard going, leave it for now. You can come back to it later. It is only obscure because it is impossible to write down everything.

And then you are not so familiar with these matters as we are. I am longing to see you.

## 15

*Paris, 17 September 1761*

I am in a terrible state. I am only writing to stop you worrying. You know how injustice and unreason make me suffer. Well, just imagine that I have had to endure a storm which took two hours to subside. And what on earth can the woman[1] hope to gain by making me burst a blood-vessel or turning my brain? What a trial life is! How often I would gladly see the end of it!

Do not be offended by these feelings of mine. You are far away and my heart is still swollen with anger. In three or four hours I shall be asleep. Tomorrow I shall find that love is still there at the bottom of my soul, even though now it is full of agonizing impatience and indignation. As I sleep, the Furies will leave me. Love will return with all his gentle train, and I shall no longer wish to die. I was pitying you for being separated. Now I pity you for being together without tasting this happiness.

I felt just as you did about Clarissa's will and funeral. This proves yet again how alike our two souls are. The only difference is that my eyes filled with tears, I could no longer read, I got up and began to lament, apostrophizing the brother, the sister, the father, the mother, and the uncles, and talking out loud, to the great astonishment of Damilaville, who didn't understand a word of my passionate speeches and asked me what was wrong. It is quite true that reading of this sort is very unhealthy after meals. You choose your time badly; you ought to read before going out walking. There is not a letter in the book which would not provide two or three texts for a moral discussion.

Uranie, Uranie, you are neglecting your health, dear sister. You are ruining your stomach and destroying your strength for good. You will be an invalid in the prime of your life and you will be leaving us just when the little savage needs your advice, your kindness and your help. It was when Telemachus was on Calypso's island that he needed Minerva, and you are in danger of abandoning him just on the threshold of the magic cave. You are a reasonable woman. Life is a bad thing. We both agree with you about that. But is it our duty to preserve it in the interests of those to whom we have had the misfortune to give it.

No, I am in no hurry to have those fragments; you can send them back whenever you like. I was on the point of going to La Chevrette and renewing my acquaintance with my pigeons, my geese, my hens, my ducklings, and the dear old cenobite. But I have had to put it off. I have just had a peremptory note from Grimm which hurt my over-sensitive feelings. I had agreed to

[1] Madame Diderot.

write a few lines for him about the paintings at this year's Salon. He tells me that if it is not done by tomorrow, it is not worth my while to finish it. I shall have my revenge for this unkindness, and the sort of revenge I like. I worked all day yesterday and all day today; I shall keep at it all night and all day tomorrow and at nine o'clock he will get a whole volume of manuscript.

He looks rather foolish, our poor friend Saurin.[1]

*The Cacouacs?* This was the name given last winter to everyone who used his reason to judge moral principles, everyone who noticed the blunders of the government and said so openly, everyone who dragged Briochet the father, the son and the Abbé through the mud. All you need to know now is, who is Briochet?[2] He is the first and greatest puppet-player in the world. If you follow all this you will see that I am as *cacouac* as they come, that you are rather a *cacouac*, and your sister too, and that there is hardly a decent and intelligent man who is not more or less one of the clan.

You think that Saurin will know everything one day? He won't be in the best of moods that day.

Yes, the *Clytemnestra* of the Comte de Lauraguais is in verse, and very beautiful verse in places. When he was reading it to me I said to him: 'But that is very fine, sir. Where did you learn to write so well?' They say that he has a man called Clinchant who knows how to do it. But what do I care if the fine verse is by Clinchant or the count? What matters is that it exists, and it does.

Rumours have been going around for the last few days that Mademoiselle Arnould is dead.[3] I must find out whether it is true or not. In the meantime, Abbé Raynal gave her a funeral oration by telling me about a conversation he had with Madame Portail, in which it seemed to me that the lady played the part of the harlot and the little actress that of the respectable woman. 'But, mademoiselle, you have no diamonds?' 'No, madam, I can't see that they are really essential for a woman living in the Rue du Four.' 'Have you an allowance then?' 'An allowance! Why should I have an allowance, madam? Monsieur de Lauraguais has a wife and children and a position in the world to keep

[1] Saurin's wife was notoriously unfaithful.

[2] God—see Voltaire's *Pot-Pourri*.

[3] Sophie Arnould (1744–1802), an actress, was at this time the mistress of the Comte de Lauraguais.

up; I do not think I could decently accept even the smallest part of a fortune to which others have a greater right than I have.' 'Upon my word, if I were in your place, I would leave him.' 'I dare say. But he is fond of me and I am fond of him. Perhaps it was foolish of me to take him, but since I have done so, I will stay with him.' I can't recall the rest. All I can remember is that the judge's wife was as despicable as the actress was admirable.

Your religion and your moral principles are excellent. Mine are just the same and I am satisfied with them. Goodbye, dear ladies. Are you beginning to glimpse a distant possibility of returning to Paris? I kiss you both, Madame Le Gendre on her rosy cheeks, for she alone has the secret of keeping fresh healthy skin and rosy cheeks when she is ill.

## 16

*Paris, 2 October 1761*

They arrived in Paris just as I was leaving, so I didn't see them.[1] But when I got back from the country I found two notes, one from him and one from her.

I spent two days at Massy with Monsieur and Madame Le Breton.[2] We went walking together. Madame is quite mad, not at all what her age, her piety and her reputation would lead you to expect. I should like to know what she was like as a young woman. She was a great friend of a certain Madame de la Martelière. If the proverb is anything to go be, that tells you all you need to know about her. You know, or perhaps you don't know, that I sometimes amuse myself by playing the passionate lover with her. She is not taken in by this, neither is her husband, but it sets us off on some merry and amusing conversations. The cold weather is beginning. Yesterday we were all sitting round a good fire, made of the wood from an old barrel. It so happened that on the plank nearest to us we could see the flaming bung-hole. The crazy old thing said to me: 'There you are, philosopher, you have been asking for my favours for a long time now. This is your chance. Just go and purge yourself in that fire and I will take you.'

[1] Grimm and Madame d'Épinay.
[2] Monsieur Le Breton was the principle publisher behind the *Encyclopédie*.

The cenobite is a very contented character who has settled in a corner of the farm-yard. He drinks, he eats, he grows plumper every day. He does not go out often. I cannot tell you if he meditates much. I believe he belongs to the Epicurean sect. His cheerfulness when he leaves his cell gives me a high opinion of the way he spends his time at home. We used to visit him twice a day. You may be certain that he took very little interest in us. When he first came, he was very young and had no name. I christened him Antonio or Dom Antonio. It is the farmer's wife who looks after him and feeds him. He is not fastidious. It is true that he often grunts, but this is less out of bad temper than because he is made like that. If you are interested in knowing the rest of his life-story, I can find out about it. I am not an inquisitive person. I enjoy people's company without bothering who they are or where they come from.

One day when I was remarking to my hostess at Massy how surprised I was by her changes of mood, she gave a curious reply: 'My word', she said, 'it is because there is no one who is really devout, only hypocrites. You can kneel and pray and keep vigil and fast and put your hands together and lift up your eyes and your heart to heaven as much as you like', she went on, 'but you won't change nature. People remain what they are. A man may put on a blue costume, fix an epaulette on his shoulder, hang a long sword at his side, cover his hat with plumes, but for all his haughty walk, his head held high and his threatening looks, he is only a coward with all the outside appearances of a brave man. When I am quiet and serious and demure, it means that I am not being myself. I have a church face, a society face, a shop face, and a face for dealing with servants. That is the acting side of me. Then there is my real life, my true self, my natural face; I don't show it so often, but it is something quite different. I don't keep it on for long, but while it is there I say all sorts of mad things, and I only stop because I can still hear my mother saying to me: "Really, little girl!" Then I close up, and down comes my veil. When I am myself with other people, I almost always repent of it in church. Even so, the people I like best are the ones with whom I find it easiest to revert to my natural immodesty. When I have to restrain myself, I am as sweet and demure as a sugar plum.'

The little Comte de Lauraguais has gone off and left Mademoiselle Arnould. Instead of lying back voluptuously in the lap of one of the most charming girls there is, he lets himself be pushed and dragged along by his silly vanity from Paris to Montbard and from Montbard to Geneva.[1] He went off with a sheaf of beautiful verse which someone else wrote for him but which he will write out again when he is with Voltaire so as to persuade him that he is the author. He is an odd creature. He has two young chemists on his payroll. One day he gets up at four in the morning. He goes and wakes them up in their garrets. He puts them in his carriage. Before they are properly awake, six horses have galloped them to Sèvres. He takes them into his little country house. Once he has them there, he tells them: 'Here you are, gentlemen. I want a discovery. You will not leave here until it is made. Goodbye, I shall be back a week from now. You have utensils, furnaces and coal. Food will be brought to you. Now work.' Having said this, he locks the door on them and off he goes. He comes back; the discovery is made. They tell him about it, and straight away he is convinced that it is his. He boasts about it. He is as proud as can be of it, even when he is with the two poor devils who really made it; as for them, he treats them like stupid fools and lets them go hungry. It wouldn't be so bad if he had said: 'You have genius and no money. I have money and I want to have genius. Let us make a deal; you get the bread and butter and I get the fame.'

I shall not get away from Paris this autumn. It is one burden after another. I am ruining my eyes peering at plates covered with figures and letters, and in the middle of this exhausting work there is the bitter thought that all I shall get for it will be insults, persecution, humiliation, and suffering; delightful, isn't it? Friend Grimm can preach away as much as he likes, he won't make an ounce of difference; I can't continue to live on the incense of posterity. A delicious meal, a touching book, a walk in a cool and solitary spot, a conversation where you open your heart and give your emotions free rein, a strong feeling which brings tears to your eyes, makes your heart beat faster, takes your breath away, and plunges you into an ecstasy, whether it comes from hearing of a generous deed or from the love you feel for someone, health, gaiety, freedom, leisure, comfort; these

[1] Montbard was the home of Buffon, author of the *Histoire naturelle*; Voltaire lived near Geneva.

are the things that make up true happiness. I shall never be happy in any other way.

But I have to think ahead a little and prepare for the time when my little girl's eyes are opened and her bosom grows rounder, her light-heartedness disappears and she grows thoughtful, and feels a strange agitation in her senses and a mysterious desire in her heart. That will be the time for dreams at night, concealed sighs and furtive glances at men by day; and that will be the time when my little fortune will have to be divided into two. I must make sure that what I give her and what I keep for myself is enough to live on comfortably. That means earning another five or six hundred francs a year; a comedy or two, a tragedy or two, and three or four good marriages on the stage will make one good one in real life.

Goodbye, my dears. Stick to your ideas about *Clarissa.* You can be sure that you are in the right. Morphyse has one or two little prejudices which lead her astray. I embrace you both with all my soul. The feelings of love and friendship which you inspire in me are and always will be the most precious part of my happiness.

## 17

*Paris, 12 October 1761*

Let me begin with the news. This time it is something which is certain if anything ever was. All the letters from Spain and from Lisbon and all the rumours in town are agreed about it. The great affair of the Portuguese Jesuits is over at last. After being tried in the first instance by the tribunal of the Inquisition and then sent before the secular judges, they have been burned alive, twenty-seven of them, together with six Jews and two Frenchmen who were in the same conspiracy. Nothing less than this was needed to vindicate the actions of Carvalho. Now we must wait for the report of the trial.

No, my dear, I only received your bouquet on the day after my name-day.[1] I was none the less glad to have it. Even if the good wishes you send me meant much less to you, I should still believe them to be sincere.

[1] St. Denis's day, 9 October.

I was due to go off to Le Grandval on Tuesday with friends Grimm, d'Alainville, and Montamy. I announced that I was going. As I spoke, I could see what long faces the mother and child were making. The child had prepared a compliment for the occasion and after all the trouble of learning it, she did not want it to be wasted; and the mother had planned a grand dinner for Sunday. Everything worked out all right. I had my trip and came back for the speeches and celebrations. My daughter made a sweet little speech; in the middle of it there were some hard words and she stopped and said: 'It's because I am gap-toothed, papa.' And sure enough, she has two front teeth missing. Then she went on. As she was getting to the end of her speech and the moment where she had to hand me a bouquet, she couldn't find it, so she stopped again and said: 'What a silly nuisance! My carnation has got lost now.' But she went on undeterred and got to the end, then she went to look for her flower, which put the finishing touch to her compliment.

Yesterday we had a grand ceremonial dinner. Madame had invited all her friends. I was very gay. I ate, I drank. At table I did the honours perfectly. After dinner, I played cards. I did not go out. I saw everyone home between eleven and twelve o'clock. I was charming, and if you only knew who with! What faces, what people, what talk, what merriment! Madame had been in fear and trembling about the way I would behave with them. She did greater justice to my taste than to my willingness to please. In fact, she hasn't seen much evidence of either.

They get here as best they can, your letters, and the same is true of my replies. But let us not worry about these annoyances which we can do nothing about; assume that I reply as regularly as you write.

You did well to go walking. The healthy sort of walk is the sort I take in the country, the sort which shakes up your whole body, and not walking up and down in the Palais-Royal, which tires you without really exerting you.

Just let me catch you executing anyone else without knowing how far he is guilty, what the relation is between the crime and the punishment and what the guilty man would have done in the future.[1]

[1] Diderot is referring to Sophie's violent condemnation of some of the characters in *Clarissa*.

If the piece *Concerning Probabilities*[1] has not been sent off to the Queen of Sweden, to Prince Ferdinand, or to the King of Prussia (for those are my friend's correspondents), I shall send it to you. Uranie shall read the one about inoculation in due course. And you shall have your Scottish songs too. I have the complete collection.[2] The ones which have been translated are very fine, and the others almost as good. But the strange thing is that they are almost all songs of love and death. When I can I will translate the first one for you; it is called *Shilric and Vinvela*. The thing that amazes me is that the songs are in very good taste, and at the same time incredibly simple, forceful, and passionate. A soldier going off to the wars says to his beloved: 'My friend, give me your father's helmet.' The girl replies: 'Here are his sword, his breastplate and his helmet. Oh, my friend, my father was wearing this armour when he lost his life.'

I am going to dine with my young Germans on Thursday; they are charming boys. I do not need to alter the tragedy they translated for me.[3] I am sure you will like it as it is; you shall have it very soon.

No, my dear, whatever you say, I can only be mistrustful up to a certain point. To be wrong in not trusting someone makes me feel too ashamed. They[4] are dealing fairly with me. That is enough for me. I merely take care to write my receipts in such a way that it would never be possible to take unfair advantage of them.

Yes, Uranie is my good friend and thinks highly of me. Even so, she did not stoop to add a flower to your bouquet.

Don't tell me that you are starting again on those damned domestic chores which made you so ill previously.

Monsieur Bertin has not made it up and never will. His friends will take good care of that.

My library will add another six or seven hundred francs a year to my income. I do not mind whether it is taken away or left with me for the time being.

Did you know that we have been excommunicated for more

[1] A short piece written by Diderot for Grimm's *Correspondance Littéraire*.

[2] The Scottish songs are Macpherson's forged *Fragments of Ancient Poetry* (allegedly by Ossian), which appeared in 1760; Diderot gives a very rough version of some lines from Fragment 4.

[3] Lessing's *Miss Sarah Sampson*.

[4] The publishers of the *Encyclopédie*.

than eighteen months now? It is the Lucca edition of our work which we have to thank for this, and it is the malevolence of our enemies which rakes it up now that everything is settled and we are going to publish come what may.

That's right, she says all that in front of her husband. She is on the wrong side of fifty and considers herself *hors de combat*, so she can say what she likes with impunity.

The little clown is back from Geneva.[1] He spent a week there with Voltaire. 'We did well to part company', he says. 'Two great poets cannot live together any longer than that.' The funny thing is not so much what he says as the way he believes it. He has written two nonsense-poems and a satirical rigmarole about the desertion of Mademoiselle Arnould. When they come out, he will have forgotten all about. it. For the time being, to do him justice, he seems to be in despair. Even if it is only his vanity which is suffering, he has a lot of that and it is very sensitive.

Grimm, Damilaville, and I have had a little disagreement. They were going to the theatre and I had to go elsewhere on business. They were sulking when I left them.

Farewell, my love. Keep well. Love me as I love you. Here is another question for you. A criminal on the run goes to consult a lawyer and asks if he is safe to give himself up. The lawyer looks into his case and says yes, he will get him out of it. Not a bit of it. The prisoner is in danger of being hanged. Knowing the peril he is in, he sends for his lawyer. He says to him: 'But they say I shall be hanged, sir.' 'I knew you would be', replies the lawyer. 'It is no more than you deserve.' Did this lawyer act well or badly? That should keep you arguing for three days and nights without stopping.

I kiss you a hundred, a thousand times.

## 18

*Paris, 14 July 1762*

How is it that I have just received your seventh letter when you have only had four of the nine I have written you, including this

[1] The Comte de Lauraguais.

one? But let us not worry about the speed of the post; it will never go as fast as we want. Passionate lovers would like the whole world to run according to their wishes.

What a lot of things I have to tell you, some of them happy and others sad. My letters are a more or less faithful history of my life. Without meaning to, I am doing what I have so often wished for. Why, I said, an astronomer will spend thirty years of his life on top of an observatory, his eye glued day and night to the end of a telescope, simply to determine the movement of a star, and no one makes a study of himself, no one has the courage to keep an accurate record of all the thoughts that come into his mind, all the feelings that agitate his heart, all his sorrows and joys. In this way century after century will go past without anyone knowing whether life is a good or a bad thing, whether human nature is good or evil, and what makes up happiness and unhappiness. But it would need a lot of courage to reveal everything. One might find it easier to accuse oneself of planning a great crime than to admit harbouring petty or low or despicable feelings. It might be less difficult to write in one's confessions: 'I desired the throne at the expense of its present occupier's life', than to write: 'One day when I was at the baths among a crowd of young men, I noticed a youth of unusual beauty and I could not prevent myself from going close to him.' This sort of self-analysis would have its uses for the writer too. I am sure that in the long run one would be anxious to have nothing but good things to enter in the record each evening. But what about you, would you reveal everything? Try asking Uranie the same question, for there is absolutely no point in committing yourself to a plan of sincerity which frightens you. As for me, far away from you as I am, there is nothing which brings me closer to you than to tell you everything and by my words to make you a spectator of my life. I don't know whether you won't already find something like this in some of my letters—and perhaps something too of what I am about to write. But what of it!

I promised you foolish things and serious things. Here are the foolish ones to start with. Madame d'Houdetot, who has innumerable hobby-horses of every shape and size, had bored her husband to distraction with her chatter about painting, sculpture, music, poetry, eloquence, love, solitude, the countryside, and all the other things with which she surrounds herself so as to be always happy and excited. Note that the husband only likes horses and gambling, which, as you can imagine, had not been mentioned once. In his annoyance he waits until the flood has subsided, gets up and says: 'Personally, I have no taste, thank God.' And she comes back at him immediately: 'Personally, I have every taste there is, thank God.' What do you think of that?

Some time ago now, I can't remember if it was in town or in the country, I heard her saying at supper: 'Every moment of the day I acquire some new taste, and I never lose a single one.' I was still in the drawing-room with Madame d'Holbach and I said to her apropos of the countess's innumerable tastes: 'Upon my word, I would prefer one solid one.' 'So would I', said the Baroness.

When I have dinner on the island,[1] which is not as often as I am asked, we sometimes amuse ourselves playing draughts. One day not long ago I was having a game with Damilaville. There was a good move he could make, but he didn't notice it and his lady friend gave him a push with her foot to make him see it. But instead of making use of her advice, he deliberately made a wrong move and said quite sharply to her: 'Don't push me, madam; I never make a move which is pointed out to me.' She was all shamefaced and assured me that this was the first time she had ever done anything of the kind, but I maliciously said that I didn't believe a word of it and that I was very pleased to learn why I had lost so many games, at which she burst into tears. I didn't want a trivial matter like this to take such a serious turn. The husband and the lover went off. I stayed with her and tried to calm her silly head, but it wasn't an easy business. According to her, Damilaville had compromised her and made her look ridiculous and this little kick, which she described as a terrible fault, would ruin her in my eyes. The only way I could find of comforting her a little was to swear that if it had been me sitting next to the woman I loved, it would have happened not once but a hundred times. 'Do you really mean it?' 'Really.' 'You are only saying that to console me.' And so to stop her tears I launched into a series of lies, for I know quite well that if I saw my Sophie about to lose a fortune by playing the wrong card, I would do nothing to stop her. What folly to

[1] The Ile Saint-Louis where Damilaville lived. His 'lady friend' was Madame Duclos.

want even Chance to favour the one you love, and to want him to beat everyone else at dice, cards, or roulette! If such little successes improve our opinion of a man, it follows that an insignificant loss will lower him slightly in our esteem. I should not be sorry to appear incompetent or even ridiculous in certain trivial matters. Woe to the woman who wants her lover to be a prodigy in every way!

So you think that I really love you? And what makes you think this, pray? Have I lived my life beside you? Have you seen me devoting myself entirely to your happiness? Have I nursed you when you were ill, comforted you when you were unhappy, helped you when you were poor? Have I envied all those about you the privilege of doing your hair, dressing you, and serving you? Do you know the hundredth part of my passion for you? Only I know how much I love you. You do not know it and never will. It seems to me that my feelings are proof against all the trials of life. Yes, my heart I am satisfied with, but all the rest is pitiful, extremely pitiful. How glad I am that you do not know your own value, and all that a lover like me is capable of doing. Oh my dear, love and friendship are not the same for me as they are for other men. When once I have said in my heart: 'I am her lover, I am her friend', you might well be alarmed if I told you all that goes with this. This is how I see it, my dear: either love and friendship are worthless, or else they will make us follow the one we love to the final ordeal, and even on to the . . . No, you of little soul, I will not finish; I do not want to make you shudder. Love, friendship, and religion are the source of the most violent passions in life.

In one of my recent letters you will find a conversation between Madame Duclos and me. I could not get it out of my head for several days, and I cannot tell you the ideas it gave me. Others might think them odd, but Uranie and you will be able to see the truth in them. I have been thinking that a man whose behaviour when wealthy was as sublime as I imagine Damilaville's would be, might be afraid that he would demean himself if he continued to seek the pleasures of love. He would fear that people might attribute his noble actions to this single petty motive. If ever he returned to his mistress's arms, it would be very infrequently and in special circumstances which excused everything. Thus one day he might be sitting with his love, they might recall the beginnings of their friendship, and their hearts would beat faster, they would look tenderly at one another and press one another's hands, kisses would be given and returned, a few tears would be shed, and it might end in a sweet moment of weakness. Do you imagine that a charming girl's benefactor who has any sort of delicacy dares speak to her of gallantry and love? If he did, what sort of name should we give to his kindness? And how could she accept it?

Here's another thing—for when I write to you, I talk as if I were by your side, with one arm on the back of your chair, chatting to you. There is no order or plan or logic in what I write; I put down everything that happens both inside and outside the space occupied by my life, both where I am and where others move about me, both where I feel constantly that I love you to distraction, and where everyone else torments themselves for a thousand and one silly trifles. So conscience is never totally depraved? Does there always come a time then when unhappiness awakens remorse in us? Come then, brigands and villains, come and listen to one of your troop on the brink of the precipice where his vices have led him, and where shame and despair await you. It is Gaudet I am thinking of as I write this.[1] How cruelly clear his faults were to him, my dear! But unfortunately continuing adversity, though it make the virtuous man tire of doing good, never brings the evildoer back to virtue. Let a fierce animal out of the trap where it is caught, and it will do its best to devour you.

I have come to an arrangement with my publishers. I find my work less of a burden now that I am spurred on by the hope of getting together a dowry for my daughter. Previously her mother loved luxury enough for two . . . But it's no good going on with that story. The audience to whom you have destined my letters will make me watch my step, because I shall no longer be talking to you alone, and the letters will be none the worse for that. I shall give praise more readily and be slower to criticize.

The sale of my library is still undecided. Pissot, my bookseller, has valued it at sixteen thousand, one hundred and eighty-five francs, less the price of a few books which the buyers asked me for and which the bookseller is supplying.

Grimm is in a wretched state. He is concealing his unhappiness

[1] Gaudet was Damilaville's superior in the Tax Department.

deep in his heart. He is losing his health. He is definitely going blind. I wrote to him today. What a letter it was, my love! In it you would have seen a true friend, depicted with those vivid, moving and delicate touches by which you were once so happy to recognize your lover. Immediately afterwards he arrived from La Briche. How glad we were to embrace one another! I kissed those eyes, and do not be jealous that I kissed them over and over as if they had been yours, those beautiful eyes where once I used to see the transparency of the sky, and which are doomed to darkness now. Would you believe it, that I had summoned him from La Briche to make him unhappy? I'll tell you why. Your affection makes you interested in everything that concerns me. Whatever I tell you about, I am always opening my heart to you and you can always see my passion hidden in some corner.

Last Sunday, I went to dinner at the Baron's, where I hadn't shown my face for more than a fortnight. There were seventeen or eighteen of us at table, but by half-past six I was left alone with the Baron, as often happens. He reproached me with not going to see him and his reproaches affected me. There are moments when this man's heart sets up a powerful resonance in me. After dinner we got into his carriage and went for a drive on the Petit Cours. He looked worried. Just imagine that some fellow, whom I shall call either a busybody or a villain when I know who it was, had taken it into his head to inform him that Madame d'Épinay was giving Grimm a terrible time and that she suspected Madame d'Holbach of stealing her lover, and her lover of seducing his friend's wife. No sooner had his suspicions been aroused than the Baron went off to ask his wife for more details. The Baroness, whose conscience was quite clear, told him all she knew. She admitted that she had often seen Madame d'Épinay in a bad mood, that Grimm's friendly behaviour towards her had won him sour looks from his mistress, that Madame d'Épinay and Madame de Maux had made far from equivocal remarks to her, that she had taken no notice of them, but had still resented being insulted, that certain people must be very used to criminal behaviour to suspect others of it on such slight evidence, that now he knew the truth, even though she had not wanted to tell him, and that whatever he decided to do, she would go along with it. The Baron gave his wife and friend their due. As for Madame d'Épinay, he seems determined to break with her. He is particularly angry, and rightly so, at the way she confided her jealous thoughts to Madame de Maux. If this lady starts gossiping, just think what the enemies who are all around spying on us will say. It would be nothing if they were the people concerned, but they will build it up into a real crime in us, since they are so envious of our good reputation. Can't you just hear them: 'So that's how philosophers carry on', etc. etc. I had foreseen how upset Grimm would be to see this friendship break up, since he had brought them together and regarded the Baron's house as a pool where his mistress would be happy to bathe on her return from Geneva. I thought it was my duty to tell him what had happened. Now he knows everything. We have schemes for a reconciliation. Will we succeed or will we fail? With such vacillating characters it is impossible to tell. It is certain that the Baroness is deeply hurt. She, her husband and Suard[1] have gone to Sannois, to see Madame d'Houdetot. The same road goes to La Briche. They will pass Madame d'Épinay's door. I asked Madame d'Holbach if they would not stop there for a rest. 'That is not what I intend', she answered stiffly.

In the rest of our conversation I was able to discuss freely with Grimm his extremely familiar way of behaving with Madame d'Holbach. I did not hide from him that if Madame d'Épinay was anything like me, she would have had cause enough for alarm, that if she had been patient enough to say nothing about it, I admired her, but that in her place I would have broken the ice long ago and either forced him to change his ways or scratched out his two bad eyes. He is so serious and sensible. To him we are like so many little children. Believe me, my dear, if this man and Uranie ever meet, they will love one another and they will regard us with pity from morning till night; and I do not like being pitied. So we must not let them meet.

This is my life. What a series of troubles! And this poor Grimm, what will he gain by his common sense, his wonderful prudence, his caution, his heart which keeps such perfect time with his head, like the hand of a clock whose movement depends on the regular swing of a pendulum? Does the consciousness that our suffering is not deserved diminish it? They say it does; so be it.

1 Jean-Baptiste Suard (1734–1817) was a member of the Holbach coterie and subsequently co-editor of the *Gazette de France* and a member of the Academy.

The saints are even able to take joy in the tribulations which God inflicts on them. I advise you to acquire a tincture of this fanaticism. The more Morphyse makes you suffer, the more highly you will think of yourself.

Your abbot from Moncetz is the Father Cyprian of Collé's extravaganza.[1] It fits exactly. He is a man totally without religion. He secretly thinks virtue ridiculous. He regards the rest of us, the virtuous, as so many dupes. I'd bet that if one day at table you said as much to him jokingly, he would not protest overmuch, particularly if you were cunning enough to hint that you too were rather inclined to think the same way.

I really must call at the Rue des Vieux-Augustins one of these mornings. But it is time for dinner now. They are calling me to come. For the last two hours I have been in my workshop at Le Breton's writing you this long and tedious epistle which you will have quite a job deciphering. Just skip everything which makes you rub your spectacles on your sleeve. All that matters is these last few words: I count on your love, and my love will last as long as my life. The rest is meaningless. Goodbye, my dear. When are you expecting your sister?

## 19

*Paris, 12 August 1762*

Here is the Jesuits' funeral notice, my dear. I have chopped it as short as I can so that they don't recognize it in the post, but I have numbered all the pages. This affair rids me of a great number of powerful enemies. Who would have guessed it, a year and a half ago? With all the time they have had to prepare their defence, they must have had very little influence or else the king must have been very set on destroying them—most likely the latter. The Portuguese business probably made him see the French affair in a new and sinister light; I imagine he was just waiting for the moment to get rid of people whom he saw as a constant threat, since they had already struck at him once, and

[1] 'Le Père Cyprien' was a fashionable parody song by Charles Collé (1709–93).

the scandalous bankruptcy of Father La Vallette will have seemed a good opportunity.[1]

They had a finger in too many pies. In the two hundred years since they were set up, there's hardly been one of them who wasn't mixed up in some notorious crime. They stirred up trouble between Church and State. Being subject to the most extreme form of despotism inside their order, they were the most abject supporters of despotism in society as a whole. To the people, they preached blind obedience to the king and to the king, papal infallibility, so that being the masters of one soul, they would be the masters of all. They recognized no authority except that of the general of their order. He was their Old Man of the Mountain. Their system is simply Machiavellianism reduced to a set of rules. In spite of all this, they could have been saved if they had had just one man of the stature of Bourdaloue;[2] but they had no one.

The funniest thing is to see the innocent way the Jansenists are gloating over their enemies' downfall. They don't realize what oblivion they will fall into. It's like the fable. Two roof-beams which propped one another up had a quarrel. The master of the house, growing impatient with their wrangling, knocked one of them down, and down fell the other. The discontented bishops are not such fools.

This Jesuit storehouse contained all sorts of wares, good and bad alike, but it was well stocked. The storekeepers were great charlatans. They gathered lots of people around them and St. Peter's affairs prospered. All this is very funny for the philosophers. Another thing is that the good Fathers kept on hoping until the very last minute, to judge by the surprise and consternation on their faces when they heard the sentence. Many of them had the look of convicted criminals. One man I know was living with them because of his job and various circumstances; he had no great love for them, but he couldn't stand the sight of their despair and left them. Today they are still pitied; tomorrow they will have songs made up about them and the day after they will be forgotten. Such is the charming character of the French nation.

[1] The Jesuits had been expelled from Portugal. In 1762, after a series of law cases, the Society was dissolved in France. They had been among the bitterest enemies of the *Encyclopédie*.

[2] A celebrated Jesuit preacher at the court of Louis XIV.

Yesterday (Wednesday) they spent all the morning saying mass and having mass said in their three churches and praying God to preserve them, but he didn't answer their prayers. Between 11 and 12 o'clock, there was a horde of devout women in their courtyard, wringing their hands, tearing their bonnets and howling like mad things. You can imagine what a stir it has caused here. We are expecting a third sentence from the high court in a few days time, but I don't know what it concerns; immediately afterwards there will be a royal edict confirming the sentences of the high court.

I can just see and hear Voltaire now. He is lifting up his eyes and hands to heaven and saying: *Nunc dimittis servum tuum, Domine, quia viderunt oculi mei salutare tuum.* Strange fellow—he has just written something called *A Eulogy of Crébillon.*[1] Some eulogy! You will see; it is the truth, but even the truth offends me when it is spoken by the mouth of envy. I cannot forgive that sort of pettiness in such a great man. He can't stand pedestals. He is working just now on an edition of Corneille. I am prepared to bet that it will be full of notes which are really so many satirical thrusts. However hard he tries and however much he belittles others, there will always be at least a dozen people in France who will be head and shoulders above him without needing to stand on tip-toe. In everything he does he comes second.

But that's enough about other people; time for a word about me. I spend my days between two sickrooms; my wife and her maid are indisposed and Madame Duclos is seriously ill, as I predicted. She has a tightness in her throat which won't be cured; all the oils and gargles and swallows nests[2] of the Sainte Chapelle will not help her.

If only Morphyse would take pity on the young man and let his impatience cut your stay short. Your return to Paris is the centre of my life.

I have that copy of Rousseau's book.[3] What shall I do with it? Pack it up and send it to you?

I haven't even set eyes on that Comus who has them all puz-

[1] Prosper Crébillon, tragedian, censor, and Voltaire's rival, died in June 1762.

[2] Swallows' nests were considered a remedy for throat infections, according to the *Encyclopédie.*

[3] *Émile.*

zled with his conjuring tricks; he's certainly not a sorcerer and that's enough for me.

I am sure your dear sister hasn't forgotten me, but you often forget to tell me that she still remembers me. Yet you know quite well how much I like to be told of it. So you have seen your dear sister and embraced her! How happy you must have been! How your two hearts must have beaten! How jealous Morphyse must have been watching you! She will have grown twice as cold as usual towards the one and twice as bad-tempered towards the other. I am sure she is paying you back now for the coldness there will be in the next two or three letters I shall receive.

Believe me, it's not easy to act against your character and make yourself a dwarf, so as to be on a level with other people and persuade them that they are quite as clever as a man who has a reputation for cleverness, and put them at their ease.

It is a *gutta serena* that Grimm is in danger of. I can tell you in advance that his dog and stick are all ready for him.

The business with the Abbé Raynal[1] has fallen through. They didn't give a damn for me and they try and tell me that Raynal didn't promise me a thing of what I say. I haven't been too badly let down, as I wasn't banking on it. With a little more time to waste, I should perhaps have built a lot of castles in the air which I should have been sorry to see evaporating. That's one of the great advantages of being busy; the busy man is less inclined to be deceived by hope; he is too occupied by the present to waste his eyes staring into the distant future. Place and time and space don't exist for a man buried in thought. A hundred thousand years of meditation would pass in a flash, like a hundred thousand years of sleep, except for the tiredness which tells us roughly how long we have been concentrating.

Farewell, my dears. I embrace you with all my heart. How quickly the days pass now! Allow me to save myself the trouble of dating this letter, my love; you can be sure that I write to you without fail every Sunday and every Thursday.

[1] Guillaume-Thomas Raynal (1713–96) was editor of the *Mercure de France*. Diderot was to have received 1500 francs a year for a monthly article in this journal.

## 20

*Paris, 2 September 1762*

*Thursday*

Before I go on with my journal, I should like to tell you about a conversation sparked off by the word *instinct*, a word which we use all the time, both in questions of taste and morality, but never define. My argument was that it is nothing but the result of innumerable minute experiences which begin on the day we first see the light and continue until the day when, secretly influenced by this long training which we no longer remember, we pronounce such and such a thing to be good or evil, beautiful or ugly, pleasant or unpleasant, without having any clear idea of the reasons for our favourable or unfavourable judgement.

Take Michelangelo deciding what shape to give to the dome of St. Peter's in Rome. This is one of the most beautiful shapes he could have chosen. Everyone is impressed and delighted by its elegance. The width was given; his first task was to decide on the height. I can see the architect trying all sorts of solutions, making the dome higher, then lower, until finally he hit on the height he was looking for and cried: 'That's it'. When he had found the right height, he had to determine the curve linking this height and this width. What a lot of experiments this must have meant! How often he must have rubbed out the line he had drawn and tried another one, first rounder, then flatter, then more bulbous, until he came upon the one he used to complete his building! What taught him to choose the right shape? Out of all the lines he drew on his paper, why did he prefer one particular one to all the rest?

Thinking about these problems, I recalled that when Monsieur de La Hire of the Academy of Sciences, the great mathematician, arrived in Rome on his travels, he too was struck by the beauty of the dome of St. Peter's. But he was not content with sterile admiration. He wanted to know what the curve of the dome was, and having obtained a plan of it, he worked out its properties geometrically. Imagine his surprise when he saw that it was the curve of greatest resistance. Michelangelo, seeking to give his dome the most beautiful and elegant shape possible, had after much searching hit on the shape which he would have had to choose if he had been seeking to make it as strong and solid as possible. This raises two questions. How is it that in a dome or a vault the curve of the greatest resistance is also the curve of the greatest elegance and beauty? How did Michelangelo come to discover this curve of greatest resistance? 'It cannot be explained', they said, 'it is the result of instinct.' 'And what is instinct?' 'Oh, we all know what instinct means.'

What I say is that when Michelangelo was an urchin at school, he played with his schoolmates, and in wrestling and pushing with his shoulders, he soon felt what was the best way of leaning so as to resist his opponent's force most effectively; that in the course of living he was bound to have been obliged hundreds of times to prop up leaning objects and once again to find the most effective angle; that sometimes he had piled books one on top of the other, and when they started to topple over he had had to balance one against the other or the pile would have collapsed; and that this was how he had learnt how to construct the dome of St. Peter's according to the curve of greatest resistance.

You have a wall which is on the point of collapsing; send for a builder. When the builder has put in his props, send for d'Alembert or Clairaut and ask either of these mathematicians to find the angle at which a prop will give the greatest support to a wall with a given tilt; you will find that the builder's angle will be the same as the mathematician's.

You will have noticed that the sails of windmills are set at a slant to their axis; otherwise they would not turn. The angle of slant is such as to allow the sails to turn as easily as possible. How is it that when the mathematicians examined the angle which had been laid down by custom and tradition, they found that it was precisely the angle which would have been indicated by higher mathematics? There is calculation on the one hand and experience on the other. Provided the calculation is accurate, it is impossible that they should disagree.

Now why is it that what is useful in reality is also what we consider beautiful in works of art and imitations of nature? It is because we invariably give our approval to usefulness, or more generally to goodness. This goodness can be contained in a work without showing; in this case the work is good, but not beautiful. Or there can be the appearance of goodness, but not the reality; then the work is only superficially good, as it is only superficially beautiful. But if there is both the appearance and the reality of goodness, then the work is truly good and beautiful. We should have to imagine ourselves in another world, where all the laws of nature were different, for something that both is good and appears good not to be beautiful.

All this may seem rather dry and abstract, but I'll try to make up for it by giving you the rest of our conversation in a few words. I said: 'And yet what could be more hidden and inexplicable than the beauty of the curve of a dome? Even so, we see that it depends on a law of nature.' Someone added: 'But what can we find in nature to justify or confute the different judgements we make of faces, particularly women's faces? They seem to be quite arbitrary.' 'Not at all', I replied. 'However diverse our tastes may be in this field, this diversity can be explained. We can distinguish what is correct from what is incorrect, and demonstrate the truth of this distinction. Relate these judgements to health, the animal functions, and the passions and you will always be able to see the reason for them. This woman is beautiful; her eyebrows follow the line of her eyes; raise her eyebrows a little in the middle and you have one of the signs of pride—and pride is offensive to us. Now leave her eyebrows as they were, but make them very thick, so that they overshadow her eyes and give her a hard look—and hardness repels us. Now leave her eyebrows alone, but pull her lips forward a little, and this makes her sulky and cross; purse up the corners of her mouth and you make her affected and disdainful; make her eyelids droop and she looks sad; make certain cheek-muscles swell out a little too much and she becomes irascible; give her eyes a fixed look and she is stupid; put fire in these fixed eyes and you have a lascivious woman. This is what explains all our likes and dislikes.

'If nature has marked a face with the outward signs of a vice or a virtue, this face becomes pleasing or displeasing to us; in addition to this, we are influenced by health, which is the basic factor, and by the ability to perform the functions appropriate to a given way of life. A handsome porter is not a handsome man, neither is a handsome runner, a handsome dancer, a handsome old man, or a handsome blacksmith. A handsome man is a man who has been well endowed by nature to perform the two essential functions of life: the preservation of the individual, which calls for many qualities, and the propagation of the species, which calls for just one.

'If habit and custom have made us develop certain parts of the body to the detriment of others, we shall no longer possess the beauty of natural man, but the beauty appropriate to some position in society; a bent back, broad shoulders, short muscular arms, stocky bent legs, and loins made immense by the habit of carrying heavy loads, all these make up a handsome porter. Natural man does nothing but live and multiply; if nature makes him handsome, he will remain handsome. The Ancients seem to have wanted to show us these two extremes in two of their greatest pieces of sculpture: the Apollo Belvedere is the man of leisure and the Farnese Hercules the man used to heavy labour. In the latter everything is exaggerated; in the former there is nothing excessive, nothing which betrays a particular way of life. He has done nothing yet, but he looks capable of anything. If you want him to fight, he will fight, if you want him to run, he will run, if you want him to make love, he will make love. The good painter must first be acquainted with natural man; then he must learn the distinguishing marks of each profession.

'But let us leave living creatures and think about works of art, architecture for instance. A piece of architecture is beautiful when it is strong and is seen to be strong, and when it is visibly appropriate to its destination. Strength is here the equivalent of health in living creatures; appropriateness to a destination is the equivalent of suitability to a given way of life in human beauty. What is particularly remarkable here is the influence of local customs. If you go to Constantinople, you will find thick, high walls, flattened arches, small doors, and small windows set high up and covered with bars. It is as if a building were beautiful in proportion to its resemblance to a prison. And indeed prison is the right word for these houses where one half of the human race keeps the other half shut up.

'In Europe on the other hand, we see large doors, large windows and everything open. This is because there are no slaves; and then there is the influence of the climate. To decide which form of architecture is more beautiful, we shall have to decide between two ways of life: is it better to trust in women's good faith or to lock them up? Will a man lead a healthier and longer life in a temperate region or in the burning tropics and the frozen north?

'Imagine a dissolute young man walking in the gardens of the Palais-Royal. He sees a little snub nose, a smiling pair of lips, a pert look and an affected walk and exclaims: "What a charming creature!" I turn my back on her with disdain and gaze instead at a face on which I can see innocence, candour, simplicity, nobility, dignity, and modesty. Do you think there would be any difficulty in deciding between my taste and the young man's? His comes down to "I love vice"; and mine to "I love virtue". And it is the same with all our judgements; they all come back in the end to these two words.'

Well, there's the gist of our conversation. Developed in more detail it would make an excellent work on taste and a justification of my taste for you, dear sisters.

## 21

*Paris, 5 September 1762*

*Sunday*

I can just see all the details of your fire: the women weeping, the men working, other people standing around or rushing in all directions, children as scared as if it were the end of the world and younger children playing as if there were nothing amiss—this and all the rest of your picture. When my mind was at rest about the fate of the remaining buildings, I began to be concerned for your health. You assure me that you are all well and you are so positive about it that I am bound to believe you.

Tell Uranie that I shall never be happy with the indifference she shows for the life of a woman we love. That woman is herself. How unfairly she treats us! Can she really love us, if she is so little concerned to prolong our happiness? If she examined her conduct carefully, delicate-minded as she is, she would realize that she falls short as a mother, a daughter, a sister, and a friend. Would she allow us to behave as she does? If not, can she in all conscience allow herself to act this way?

But let us leave this refrain; I have already repeated it more than once and I shall come back to it every time I see or learn that she is not well. However she may neglect herself, she cannot lose her life at will; all she will achieve meanwhile will be to diminish her inner strength. Her physical weakness is bound to affect her other functions: she will not have that force of feeling, thought, speech, and action which a healthy body gives us and she will depart from this world without having known all she was capable of or displayed it to others. There have been moments when she was satisfied with herself; how can she neglect the means of making them more frequent?

Uranie, please forgive someone who regrets all the good which you could do and would like to do, but are prevented from doing by your constant ill-health, if he asks you what you are good for, when your stomach gives you unbearable pain, your legs give way under you, and your mind and thoughts are in a fog. You give us a fine example of stoicism, but do you not think that you could put your health to better advantage both for yourself and for us?

I have already obeyed you, my dear, and taken up my journal again in my last letter but one. I like to have you as a witness of my life and I remember only the moments which I propose to describe for you; the rest are lost.

I think I had got to our trip to La Briche. I had not been to the house there previously. It is small, but everything around it has a wild look, the water, the gardens and the park. That is the place to live, and not the gloomy and magnificent mansion at La Chevrette. There are huge ponds with steep banks, full of rushes and marsh weeds, an old ruined moss-covered bridge over the water, thickets untouched by the gardener's pruning-hook, trees growing according to the whim of nature, trees planted with no care for symmetry, fountains gushing out of openings which they have made for themselves, not a particularly large park, but one you can lose yourself in—these are the things for me. I saw the little apartment which Grimm has picked for himself; from his windows your eyes look out over the farmyard and the kitchen garden, and come to rest finally on a noble building in the distance.

Damilaville and I arrived there just as they were sitting down to table. We had a cheerful and delicious dinner. After dinner we went walking. Damilaville, Grimm, and Abbé Raynal went ahead of us, talking politics. The Abbé in particular was much preoccupied by the revolution in Russia.[1] Meanwhile I was advising Madame d'Épinay to see the Baron and his wife infrequently and gradually to break with a society where she would constantly feel upset and hurt by seeing that she was not receiving the justice which she felt was owing to her.

In the evening we were joined by Doctor Gatti, who had come to Sannois, a little village a mile or so from La Briche, to look at Monsieur de Saint-Lambert's illness; he had supper with us and took the fourth seat in our carriage home. While we were waiting for supper, we read, played cards, made music and talked; there was much talk of the affair of the Jesuits, which was hot from the press. I made so bold as to say that to judge from their history they were a band of fanatics under the despotic command of a Machiavellian leader; Abbé Raynal, who is an ex-Jesuit, was none too pleased with my definition, even though he said in one of his books that the Society of Jesus was a sword whose hilt was at Rome and whose point was everywhere.

Such is the human mind; we attack those who are flourishing, but we forget the wicked when they are in difficulties and pity them when we have nothing more to fear from them. And then we pride ourselves on either our courage or our compassion. Human vanity can feed on anything. Not that we don't forget ourselves from time to time and entertain ourselves by kicking those who are on the floor; you only need to think of what was said to Father Griffet. After a long lament about the severity with which they were being treated, he concluded: 'We are being driven out; they are stripping us of our garments, our name, our place in society, and the house where we lived surrounded by the hearts of our kings.' And someone went on: 'That's what comes of being in a bit too much of a hurry to have Louis XV's, Father.'

We got back into our carriage after supper; on the way home, it was Doctor Gatti who kept us amused. He told us all about life in Italy, climate, painting, music, architecture, sciences, manners, fine arts, and even freedom of thought. I liked one thing he said and this was that religious devotion gives spice to a woman's love. As he put it, 'you could say that she has to trample her God underfoot as she rushes into her lover's arms.

[1] Catherine II had just deposed her husband Peter III to become the only ruler of Russia; a few days later Peter was strangled.

Just think of the furious, rushing flood of passion, when once she has broken down this dam. Her religion is yet another sacrifice that she makes to her lover, and the convenient thing is that this religion, this same motive which makes her give herself to you with such delighful impetuosity as long as you enjoy her love, rids you of her when she is no longer of any use to you.'

There is no logic in conversation and it seems that the jolting of a carriage, the various things you see as you go along, and the increasingly frequent silences all contribute to make it still more disjointed. We ran through the different regions of Italy. We made a particularly long stop in Venice, and how could one fail to stop in a place where the carnival lasts for six months, where even the monks go about in masks, and where in a single square you can see on one side a stage with mountebanks performing merry, but monstrously indecent farces, and on the other another stage with priests performing farces of a different complexion and shouting out: 'Take no notice of those wretches, gentlemen; the Pulcinello you are flocking to is a feeble fool; here (displaying the crucifix) is the genuine Pulcinello, the great Pulcinello.'

Somebody, I think it was Doctor Gatti, told us two very different stories, which you will enjoy. You have to know that the senators are the most miserable slaves to their own high rank. On pain of death they are forbidden to have any conversation with a foreigner, unless they go themselves and confess that they chanced to meet a Frenchman, an Englishman or a German and exchanged a few words with him. It is a capital crime to enter the house of any ambassador, whatever court he may represent. A senator was in love with a woman of his own rank who was in love with him. Every night at midnight he went out, wrapped in a cloak, alone and without a servant, and visited her for an hour or two. To get to his lady, he had to make a long detour, or else go through the French Embassy. Love is blind to danger, and love which is shared cannot bear to waste a moment. Our loving senator did not hesitate to take the shortest route. For several months in a row he went through the French Embassy; in the end he was seen, reported, and arrested. He was interrogated; with a single word he could have ruined the honour and endangered the life of the one he loved, and saved his own. He said nothing and was beheaded. That is admirable, but had the woman who loved him the right to remain silent too?

Now here is the second story I promised you. President Montesquieu and Lord Chesterfield met during their travels in Italy. These two men were made to make friends quickly, as indeed they did. They were constantly arguing, mainly about the superior qualities of their two nations. The Lord granted the President that the French were wittier than the English, but said they had no common sense. The President admitted the facts, but claimed that there was no comparison between wit and common sense.

The argument had been going on for some days. They were staying in Venice. The President got about a lot, went everywhere, looked at everything, asked questions, talked, and made a note of all his observations every evening. One evening he had been at home for an hour or two busy at his usual task, when he was visited by a stranger, a Frenchman, rather badly dressed, who said to him: 'Sir, I am a compatriot of yours. I have been living here for twenty years, but I have always kept my affection for the French, and have considered myself only too happy on the occasions when I have been able to be of service to them, as I can be to you today. In this city one is free to do everything, except meddle in affairs of state. A single thoughtless word about the government can cost you your head, and you have already spoken hundreds. The State Inquisitors are watching your movements. You are being spied on, every step you take is followed, every word you utter is noted down, and they are in no doubt that you are writing something. I know for a certainty that you are due to receive a visit, either today or tomorrow. If indeed you have been writing, sir, take care and remember that one innocent line, maliciously interpreted, could cost you your life. That is all I had to say to you. I have the honour of wishing you good night. If you should meet me in the street, all I ask by way of reward for the important service I have done you is that you should not recognize me, and if by chance my warning comes too late and you are arrested, that you should not denounce me.'

With that, the worthy fellow disappeared, leaving President Montesquieu in a state of extreme alarm. The first thing he did was to go quickly over to his desk, take out his papers, and throw them on to the fire. A moment later, Lord Chesterfield came in. He had no difficulty in seeing the fearful state his friend was in. He enquired what had happened. The President told him about the visit he had received, the burning of his papers, and the order he had given to have his post-chaise ready at three in the morning; for his plan was to escape as quickly as possible from a place where it might be fatal to stay a moment longer. Lord Chesterfield listened unperturbed and said: 'Excellent, my dear President, but let us keep a cool head and think more calmly about your adventure.' 'Keep a cool head!', replied the President. 'Think what you are saying; I cannot even be sure of keeping my head.' 'But who was that man who so generously came and put himself in great danger so as to help you? There is something unnatural about it. He can be as French as you like, but patriotism does not make people perform such dangerous actions, particularly on behalf of strangers. The man was not a friend of yours?' 'No.' 'He was badly dressed?' 'Yes, very badly.' 'Did he ask you for money, for a few francs in exchange for his warning?' 'Not a penny.' 'That is even more extraordinary. But where did he get his information from?' 'Upon my word, I have no idea. . . . Perhaps the State Inquisitors themselves?' 'They are the most secret body in the world, and in any case your man could never have got near them.' 'But perhaps he was one of their spies?' 'Impossible. Do you think they would employ a foreigner as a spy, and that a spy would be dressed like a beggar when his trade is despicable enough to be well-paid? Or that this spy would betray his masters for you at the risk of being garrotted if you are arrested and give him away, or if you escape and he is suspected of warning you? You must be joking, my friend.' 'But who could it be then?' 'I am trying to think, but I cannot imagine.'

When they had been through all the possible explanations together, and the President persisted in his plan of getting away as soon as possible and making sure of his safety, Lord Chesterfield, who was walking up and down and rubbing his forehead like a man struck by some profound idea, suddenly stopped and said: 'Wait a moment, President: I have an idea, my friend. What if . . . by some chance . . . this man . . .' 'Yes, what about him then?' 'What if this man . . . Yes, it's possible; I am sure that must be it.' 'But who is he then, this man? If you know, tell me quickly.' 'If I know! Yes, I think I know now. . . . What if this man had been sent to you by . . .' 'By whom then, pray?' 'By a man who can be clever at times, by a certain Lord Chesterfield who perhaps wanted to prove to you experimentally that an ounce of common sense is worth more than a hundred pounds of wit, for with an ounce of common sense. . . .' 'Oh! you villain,' exclaimed the President, 'what a trick to play on me! And my manuscript! I have burned my manuscript!'

The President never forgave the Lord for this practical joke. He had ordered his post-chaise; he got into it that very night and went off without saying goodbye to his travelling companion. If I had been in his place, I should have thrown my arms round his neck and kissed him and said: 'My dear friend, you have proved to me that there are witty men in England; one day perhaps I shall be able to show you that there are sensible men in France.'[1]

There's the story, told in rather a hurry. You will be able to give it all the graces it is lacking and make a charming tale of it.

Goodbye, my dears. I embrace you with all my heart. How happy I should be if I could give you a moment's consolation for all the long and cruel anxiety you have endured. I love you both to distraction. If I were a lover to either one of you, I should certainly need the other as a friend.

I am writing this letter in the evening. Tomorrow it will be at Damilaville's, where I hope to find some papers which I shall send you, and which will prove to you that there are people unhappier than any of us, and that a wise man will think of death as a happy moment when we escape from the vice and misery which constantly lie in wait for us and which would overwhelm us if a life of several hundred years gave them the chance to do so. Dear sister, do not take unfair advantage of these last words to justify your wrongful neglect of a gift which is not yours, but is pledged to the rest of us by a hundred sacred pacts. Have not my love and I certain rights to that property? Goodbye, goodbye; I embrace you both with all my love. I will stop now, so as not to make a jest of something so serious, Goodbye.[2]

[1] The story of Montesquieu and Lord Chesterfield has no foundation in fact.
[2] I have omitted a long and uninteresting postscript from this letter.

## 22

*Paris, 26 September 1762*

*Sunday*

This illness has extraordinary ups and downs;[1] it robs her of all her strength and leaves her thin and as frail and insubstantial as a shadow. What I see of doctors and medicine day by day does not improve my opinion of the profession. To be born in a state of imbecility amid cries of pain, to be the plaything of ignorance, error, want, illness, wickedness and passion, to return gradually to a state of imbecility, to live all your life from childish stammering to senile babbling surrounded by rogues and charlatans of every kind, to expire between a man who feels your pulse and a man who nags at your mind, not to know where you have come from, what you have come for and where you are going, this is life, and they call it the greatest gift of our parents and of nature.

Some of our pleasantest times are spent with a man I have never talked to you about, Montamy. He is as well informed as any man I know and as sensible and prudent in his actions. He is attached to his duty, which comes before everything else for him, and faithful to his master, to whom he has always told the truth without offending him; he goes to mass without placing much faith in it, respects religion, but laughs up his sleeve at the jokes which are made against it, hopes for the resurrection of the dead, without having any very clear ideas about the nature of the soul, and in general is a bundle of contradictory ideas which make his conversation very entertaining.

I mention him to you, because we are going to have dinner with him next Wednesday; there will be the Baron, back from Voré,[2] the Baroness, back from Le Grandval, Grimm, back from Saint-Cloud, Madame d'Épinay, back from La Briche, and the rest of us, such as Suard, d'Alainville, and myself, who have not left Paris and who will meet again there. I like such parties, both because I enjoy them at the time and because I enjoy telling you about them.

The little Abbé[3] will be there too with his stories. I don't

[1] Madame Diderot had been very ill for nearly three weeks.
[2] The country home of Helvétius.
[3] Abbé Galiani.

know where he gets them all from, but he is inexhaustible. The last time we saw him, he told us that once a lady was dying, and dying of certain painful disease which it is a pleasure to catch, and the priest was exhorting her: 'Come now, madam, resign yourself; offer up your suffering to God.' 'That would be a pretty present to give Him', she replied. Then he told us how one day one of his friends was saying mass and he was serving at the altar. His friend was a mathematician, and therefore very absent-minded. In the middle of mass he forgets all about the holy sacrifice and starts dreaming about the solution to certain equations, and remains meanwhile with his arms raised for a considerable time to the great edification of some members of the congregation and the great boredom of others. The Abbé is one of the latter; he pulls his friend the celebrant by the chasuble. The celebrant emerges from his reverie, but cannot remember where he has got to in the service. He turns round and asks his friend: 'Have I done the consecration, Abbé?' The Abbé replies: 'Upon my soul, I have no idea.' And the priest snaps back: 'What the devil were you thinking of then?' This may not sound brilliant, but the appropriateness and the gaiety of the occasion give it an effervescence which disappears and cannot be brought back when the moment is past.

Abbé Arnaud and Suard have just been given the *Gazette de France*.[1] This will mean a small fortune for Suard. That was all he needed to provide for the happiness of the woman he is madly in love with. He will marry her if he is an honest man—and if he ignores my advice.

With all my friends scattered outside Paris, my days are fairly monotonous: getting up late, because I am lazy, going over a chapter of history and a harpsichord lesson with my little girl, going in to my workshop, correcting proofs until two o'clock, having dinner, walking, playing piquet, having supper, and beginning all over again the next morning.

Next Thursday I shall send you the two works which have been written on behalf of the Calas family.[2] It will make a big parcel, twenty-seven quarto sheets. I must ask you in advance

[1] The *Gazette* had just become the *Gazette de France* and had been taken over by the Ministry for Foreign Affairs.

[2] In March 1762 the protestant Jean Calas had been unjustly executed at Toulouse; he was rehabilitated largely as a result of Voltaire's efforts.

not to show them to anybody. If they should happen to fall into certain hands, there would be bound to be a pirated edition which would ruin the publisher.

I send you my greetings and embrace you with all my heart. It is late and I must hurry off to Le Breton's to see to our second volume of plates, which is due to appear very soon now. I hope it will be even better received than the first. The quality of the engraving is better and the subjects are more varied and more interesting. If our enemies were not the most despicable of men, they would die of shame and envy.

The eighth volume of text is nearly finished. It is full of charming things of every kind. I have sometimes felt tempted to copy out passages for you. In time this work must certainly cause a revolution in the minds of men, and I hope it will not be to the advantage of tyrants, oppressors, fanatics and bigots. We shall have served the human race; but we shall have been reduced to cold unfeeling dust, long before anyone is grateful to us.

Why not praise good men in their lifetime, since they can hear nothing from the grave? This is the moment for consoling ourselves with the prayer of the Muslim philosopher: 'Oh God, forgive the wicked; you have done nothing for them, since you let them become wicked. The good have nothing more to ask of you, since by making them good you have done everything for them.'

I am glad I thought of this, otherwise I should have been very dissatisfied with my letter. If it is gloomy, that is because my life is gloomy too.

Keep well, both of you, and continue to love me well. For the last few days I have been plunged in the maddest, wisest, and funniest book of them all.[1]

## 23

*Paris, 3 October 1762*

*Sunday*

I don't dare to predict how her illness will develop; some days are good, some days are bad, some days are terrible; one day she has a good appetite and the next she can't stand the sight

[1] *Tristram Shandy.*

of food; some of her faeces are painful and bloody, others show none of these bad signs. It's all incomprehensible; all we know is that she is becoming thinner and more depressed and losing strength all the time. But there is one symptom that I find particularly worrying, and that is her sweet temper, her patience and quietness and worst of all her renewed love and confidence in me. Neither she, nor anyone around her gets any sleep. The doctor is the only person who is always satisfied. I have an idea that he doesn't know what he is doing and that he is wrong about the cause of the ailment, but I daren't tell him so. If I should be wrong and he acted in accordance with my mistaken ideas and the change of treatment had fatal consequences, I should never get over it. The result is that from morning to night I have to give the patient things which I think are unsuitable and unlikely to help matters—if they are not actively bad for her—see the harm they do, and say nothing.

Tomorrow I shall move into the house and only go out in the evenings. I am obliged to do this so as to deal with domestic affairs, which my wife is in no state to look after, to organize my time better, and above all to see to my daughter's education which has been abandoned recently.

I am alone in Paris; the Baron, pleased as Punch, is reading his works at Voré. The Baroness, far from her admirers, is leading a boring life at Le Grandval; Madame d'Épinay is all alone at La Briche and none too happy. Grimm is racing along towards Westphalia. He is a very close friend of Monsieur de Castries, who has just been seriously wounded. He is going 250 leagues to see how he can help and comfort his friend. That's Grimm all over. He was off before I had time to say goodbye, at two in the morning, with no servant and leaving his affairs in a mess, thinking only of the distance he had to go and the danger his friend was in.

Your *cas de conscience* is not worth bothering about: can an action be wrong without some sort of injustice? Can you be acting wrongly when you do everything duty requires? Can you leave a part of your duty undone without acting unjustly in some respect?

I forgot to tell you that a fortnight ago I received by way of Prince Golitsyn[1] an invitation from the Empress of Russia to go

[1] The Russian ambassador in Paris.

and finish our work in Saint Petersburg. I am offered complete freedom, protection, honours, money, prestige, in a word everything which might tempt men dissatisfied with their native land and without any close ties of friendship to leave their country and go abroad.

I had to write back to Voltaire, who added his solicitations to those of the Russian court. At the same time he had sent me his commentary on Corneille's *Cinna*. I could only say to him that it was true, fair, interesting and beautiful, because that is what it is; I only differed from him in finding him more indulgent than I should have been; he has not picked up all the faults which I see in the play. I suppose it is because he is less conscious of the writer's difficulties than I am.[1] There is no one more offended by wickedness than those who do not know how hard it is to be good.

This morning Damilaville, Madame d'Épinay, and I are having a meeting, to see that Grimm's *Correspondence* does not suffer from his absence.

I can see, from the offers we have received, that they do not know that our manuscript is not our property, that the publishers supplied all the capital, and that we should be acting dishonestly in taking away a single page. Well, what do you say to it? It is in France, the home of civilization, science, art, good taste, and philosophy, that we are persecuted and it is from the depths of those barbarian regions of the frozen north that arms are stretched out to us. If this fact is written down in history, what will our descendants think? Isn't it the most splendid slap in the face imaginable for good Monsieur Omer de Fleury, who made that fine speech a year or two ago to have us driven out?

If I were in a different frame of mind, I should find this incident rather pleasing; but my mind is closed to every pleasant emotion. There are very few things in life which could make me smile at the moment. You are right, Uranie, all is vanity, all is illusion, and it is all hardly worth living for. I had better stop there rather than following that train of thought, which might seem in some way offensive to those I love best.

But do I have to restrain myself for fear of hurting them? And if I do restrain myself, will they be more offended by what I say,

[1] *Sic*, though the sense appears to require 'more conscious of the writer's difficulties . . .'

or by what I have at the bottom of my heart, what I think, what I feel and what I decide, even without their knowing it? I ask no better than to be happy. Is it my fault if I am not? Is it my fault if I see in everything the defects which are there and which grieve me; if all our life is no more than a lie, a succession of deceiving hopes? We learn all this too late. We tell our children, and they do not believe a word of it. They have grey hair before they too learn the truth.

Goodbye, I hope you are well. Throw away this miserable talk. If I were to disturb your pleasures, your happiness and your peace of mind for as much as a moment, I should be like the fat man, as big as six ordinary men, who was suffocating in the crowd and shouting: 'What a damn crush! what a mob! etcetera, etcetera!' Someone standing next to him said to him: 'You great walking barrel, what are you complaining about? Can't you see that there would be fifty thousand times the crush if everyone was like you?'

And here I am, possibly making everyone around me miserable and poisoning the lives of the ones I love—what right have I to grumble at life? If everyone else grumbled as much as I do, no one would be able to hear anyone speak; the world would be the most unbearable pandemonium. If everyone else was as bad-tempered, unfair, difficult, sensitive, touchy, jealous, crazy, silly, stupid, and monstrous as I am, things would be quite insufferable. So since we are no better than the people whom we call worthless, let us put up with them and be quiet. Which I hereby do. Goodbye.

Here is Mariette's speech.[1] I shall finish by making you love the country.

## 24

*Paris, 14 October 1762*

*Thursday*

Here is the way I spend my days, and you will see that it is not much less wearisome than the way you spend yours. I have an important question continually on my mind.[2] It rules my life,

[1] On behalf of the Calas family.
[2] A mathematical problem, connected with the squaring of the circle.

follows me through the streets, makes me absent-minded in company, interrupts me in the middle of my most essential occupations, robs me of my sleep at night. You remember the farce of Patelin? I am the image of Monsieur Guillaume, who constantly mixes up his cloth and his sheep when he is speaking to the judge. This question is my cloth and everything else is sheep to me. When people talk to me about sheep, I talk about sheep too, but it is not long before my cloth worms its way into the conversation.

In the morning then my cloth occupies me; I keep house, look after the child's education, and take care of her mother when the servant is out. In the middle of all this I sketch out a piece for Grimm. I have done him two delightful things, one on painting and the other on religion. The first has already been sent off, so you won't see it. I will send you the second. I forgot to mention that this damned question gives me constant *souleurs*; I keep thinking that I have gone wrong at some point. I have doubts about even the most evident truths; suddenly it seems to me that everything has collapsed or will have to be changed, and so I come back from my sheep to my cloth.

But this word *souleurs*, which in our Langres *patois* means the contracting of the heart you feel in the face of some panic terror, is it a French word or not? Still, French or not French, it makes no difference. It expresses my meaning exactly.

I dine at home, between one and two o'clock. By three o'clock I am at Le Breton's. I work there until seven or half past seven. Whether I have finished what I am doing or not, I hurry off home. I do not wish to be invited to supper by those people, because I have sworn never to eat there again, for a reason which I will tell you when I see you, but which is not worth writing down. It comes down to the fact that they are misers and place too much importance on an indifferent meal for me to be able to accept it at the price. Between eight and nine, I go to the Quai des Miramionnes in search of a letter which is not there. I call in at the corner of the Rue de la Femme-sans-Tête. It is about ten o'clock by the time I get home.

This business with Monsieur de Salignac is frightful.[1] His

[1] Monsieur de Salignac, Sophie's brother-in-law, had just gone bankrupt in criminal circumstances. Monseiur de La Fargue, a naval officer, was married to Salignac's sister.

debts are estimated at eighteen hundred thousand francs. The list includes detailed circumstances which plunge Madame de Salignac in agony twenty times a day and make your mother's heart bleed. She can see how miserable Madame de La Fargue is. She fears that it may cost Monsieur de La Fargue his position, and unfortunately this is only too probable.

It was on Tuesday evening that I saw your mother, after she had sent me a second note at Le Breton's. She was expecting me in the evening. She felt sure that I would not fail her, since she needed my help. This is what she wrote in her letter and said to me when I saw her. She seemed somewhat changed. I arrived at six o'clock. She had a fire lit in her stove. We talked for about an hour and a half, quite agreeably, about her affairs, my affairs, your health, her misfortunes, the time she intended staying here, and finally about the little favour she wanted me to do her.

Monsieur de Salignac has some connection with the Duke of Orléans. Monsieur Duval has composed a petition to be presented to the duke on Fayolle's[1] behalf and I have agreed to give it either to Abbé Omelanne or else to friend Montamy. It is a great pity that Grimm is away. He is a friend of Fontaine's, and Fontaine can obtain what he wants from the duke and would have done this for Fayolle, unless the duke's council had raised objections which you can easily imagine without my spelling them out. The circumstances and the name are inauspicious. I shall be going to see her again this morning. We shall do what we can.

Madame de Salignac knows her husband now. Would you believe that the mad old rogue had treated himself to Mademoiselle Deschamps? You will not lose any of your thirty thousand francs. Your mother would already have told you all the details of this affair, if she had thought she could safely do so.

I did not see Madame de Salignac. The seals had been removed and the whole house was full of lawyers. I hope and fear that I shall see her this morning. In the course of our conversation your mother said two things to me. The first was that she would not abandon her daughter to her troubles and her unhappiness. The second was that this affair would not be over for at least four months. What do you make of that? Will she leave you

[1] Vallet de Fayolle, Salignac's son, subsequently obtained a post in French Guiana and settled there.

by yourself at Isle for all that time? Will she send for you in Paris? What do you think?

Oh yes! forgive me, I did have some bouquets. I had one from Angélique, accompanied by a lovely flowery compliment. I had one from Madame Diderot, graciously given and graciously accepted. I had some from friends. I was given flowers at the Quai des Miramionnes and flowers at the Quai de Bourbon.

It was a rather fine morning. We hired a carriage and drove out to Maisons to see a house built by the president of the same name, who said to the famous Mansart: 'Here is space and here is money; do what you like with them.' I already knew this anecdote before going there and I imagined that the architect would have built an enormous palace. He did something far better; what we saw put me in my place and gave me the greatest admiration for the artist. He made a building which is appropriate. This chateau at Maisons is exactly the right house, not for a king, or a prince, or a financier, or a rich man, but for a first president.

The architecture is completely simple. You cannot imagine doors and windows in better taste. There are no columns, except on the garden facade, where there are one or two on the two corner pavilions. Together with this simplicity, you are constantly struck by the elegance, nobility, and delicacy of the building. It is the same with the gardens. The chateau is situated at the centre of four great broad avenues, each of which stretches for more than a league. Below the gardens, the house is surrounded by the Seine, which is really superb at that point. There are hardly any clipped trees, hardly any neat lawns, just natural woodland. On the one hand you can see the river, on the other the hills.

A feeling which I had there and have had nowhere else, was that the longer I stayed, the more I liked it and the more I found to look at and admire, because in every detail, even in the gates, I could see the appropriateness of the residence to the rank and character of the man.

I saw only one statue, not very well executed, but beautifully conceived. It is a Cleopatra, who seems to be defying Fortune; she is naked and beautiful, if beauty is compatible with such a ferocious expression; the snake is wound several times round her arms and her head and acts as a sort of head-dress.

Powerful effects always come from a mixture of the voluptuous and the terrible; for instance beautiful half-naked women offering us delicious potions in the bloody skulls of our enemies. That is the model for everything that is sublime. It is subjects like that which make the soul melt with pleasure and shudder with fear. The combination of these feelings plunges it into an extraordinary state, and it is the mark of the sublime that it moves us in a quite exceptional way.

But tell me, how can any connection or proportion be established between a pile of stones and a man's character? What is the relation founded on? I think we have to trace it back to the residence of the monarch; his palace sets the standard. Make Versailles as simple as the palace of Maisons and the palace of Maisons will be too splendid for the residence of a first president.

So much for the general character of the building and even for certain details. But there are other details which are personal and bring the man nearer to us or remind us of him. A wild place, a hidden place, and a populous place will not all do for the same person.

I said that if once the principles of morality were firmly established, this trunk would put out innumerable smaller branches which would attach even the most insignificant virtues to it. They would be like the leaves on the tree, which can be separated from it in their hundreds without any apparent loss, although in fact there is always some slight loss. If the principles of taste were established, they would extend to every trivial thing, down to the fringes of a coquette's finery. The world will be many years older before either of these tasks is completed. Yet there is nothing that is more important. They would comprise the code of goodness and the code of beauty down to the last detail.

Goodbye, good and loving friends, whom I love all the more because I do for you what the devout do for God: everything to make themselves acceptable to him. You are the guiding stars of my every thought and action. If there is a good deed to be done, I do it and say: they will hear about it and think all the more highly of me. I might perhaps be more disinterested, but I cherish your praise too much to do without it. It is true that once the praise has been given and your words have been heard, I have had my reward and the affair is completely forgotten.

I must finish, because I have to dress and run off to the Rue des Vieux-Augustins to pick up the petition. I have little hope for it, but no matter. What if things drag out and bring you back to Paris? But I must not harbour thoughts like that. It would be too cruel if I were disappointed.

A thousand kisses to you both. I shall never feel at ease with Morphyse, nor she with me. I don't know why it is. Do not forget me.

## 25

*Paris, 23 February 1765*

Even if I had made you a solemn promise, my love, I think I should have been forced to break it by circumstances that have recently arisen. But where in the world do you think I can find happiness, if not with two charming women who inspire the tenderest feelings in me, as I do in them? Monsieur Petit can say what he likes, I cannot possibly be easy in my mind and look on calmly while the woman I love takes a dose of poison every morning. You cannot imagine the effect this has on me. My position is really very difficult. How I should reproach myself if thanks to my medical reading and the opinion of professionals I knew the danger of the remedy which you are hoping will cure you and said nothing, abandoning your life and health to Petit and his cursed hemlock! But on the other hand how can I bring myself to insist further and risk dying of remorse, if your lump got worse and I knew that I had prevented you from resorting to the only possible cure while there was still time? I am bound to let you continue and wait fearfully for the result, which will make me die of grief or weep for joy. I must either worship Petit and his hemlock or detest them.

I shall be bitterly reproached for not returning the two stories as I had promised, but you make it impossible for me not to send them back to you. So give me your word that you will let me have them back here tomorrow and not let them be copied; and be sure to keep your word better than I have kept mine. I cannot be with you, but choose a moment at table, look at one another in silence and drink to my health. My love is the measure of the fear your medicine inspires in me. Think how great that must be.

## 26

*Paris, 20 May 1765*

This is the third time that Monsieur Vialet and I will have been to see Monsieur de Sartine[1] about his project, my love, and three mornings' work I shall have lost. Although I shall be at your door at midday, I shall not have the pleasure of seeing you. The same carriage which takes me to the Rue Neuve Saint-Augustin will bring me back here to deal with a huge pile of work. I really am tired of being the slave to my needs. When will the day come when I am free of every occupation except pleasing you? Never, never! I shall die without showing you how I can love.

Be sure to make my apologies to Madame Le Gendre. Everything and everyone drifts apart. A million things thrust themselves despotically in the way of the duties of love and friendship, so we do nothing properly. We do not give ourselves over completely to our ambition, or to our tastes, or to our passions, and we are continually dissatisfied with ourselves. One of the great disadvantages of life in society is the host of occupations it brings, and particularly the thoughtlessness with which we contract obligations that rob us of our happiness. We get married, we take up a position; and before we have any common sense, we have already got a wife and children. Oh, if only I could begin again! These are the regrets which are constantly on our lips; I have felt them for everything I have done, except for my sweet friendship with you, dear love. If there is something I regret, it is the time I have not been able to give to you.

I greet you and embrace you with all my heart.

Here is a bundle of letters for you to forward to their destination.

## 27

*Paris, 24 July 1765*

Sunday; no, it's a Thursday and I took it for a Sunday.[2]

[1] Lieutenant of police; his headquarters were in the Rue Neuve Saint-Augustin.
[2] Though the rest of the letter implies that it was in fact Wednesday, 24 July.

You have still only had two of my letters? And yet this is my sixth. I have numbered them all, so that we should be certain that none had gone astray. Have a look at the numbers.

My dear, do you really think I can receive three or four violent shocks in the space of two weeks without my health suffering? You will be hearing about it, unless they are afraid of worrying you. My stomach and intestines are in a wretched state. Even the lightest of soups goes straight through me. I cannot digest the yolk of an egg. Luckily I can sleep, and sleep cures everything. But how is it that a liquid which hurts me like a red-hot iron when it comes out does not give me any pain when it is inside such a tender passage? For I have absolutely no colic. My strength is completely gone however. I can feel my knees giving way under me. This weakness, which makes standing up very wearing, makes lying in bed quite blissful. Even Madame Le Gendre is no happier lying down that I am. You know how agreeable it is to sit down in an armchair when you are tired by a long walk? This is precisely what I feel when I have lowered my heavy limbs on to the mattresses. It is really the sort of self-indulgence which a devout person would feel guilty about. So you see there is nothing to worry you and in three or four days I shall be as right as rain.

But I am not the only one in the house who is ill. Madame Diderot is suffering from sciatica all along one thigh. She has been advised to rub it with a mixture of salt, spirits and soap. A few days ago when the operation was in progress I was just going into the room when my little girl ran to stop me and shouted: 'Stop, stop, papa; if you saw her, you would die of laughing.' There was her dear mama leaning over the foot of the bed with her behind up in the air and her servant down on her knees rubbing her for all she was worth. It wasn't at all like the proverb which says that it's a waste of time to soap the head of a Moor, for Madame Diderot is extremely white. It wasn't her head that was being soaped either, and she felt better for the treatment. Since that time I have been given the job once or twice and have acquitted myself very well.

We have unexpectedly lost a great artist: Charles Vanloo.[1]

At seven this evening I am going to talk with our dear sister.

[1] Carle Vanloo (1705–65) was a well-known painter and director of the Academy of Painting.

Our last two chats have been very pleasant, but so varied that I cannot remember them.

Yesterday her servant made a mistake and instead of announcing me, announced Monsieur Perronet, apparently out of force of habit.[1] She was really cross with me for being so discreet and not interrupting those *tête-à-têtes* I mentioned to you.

Today Wednesday we had planned to go with La Rue[2] to see the paintings at the Luxembourg, but do you know who stopped us going? The Princess of Nassau-Saarbrücken.[3] She had been to Calais to say goodbye to her son, who was going to England. She was returning to Saarbrücken by way of Paris, where she had only one more day, and of that day she gave the whole morning to Grimm and me. She is a charming woman, both in appearance and in character. At the beginning I was as stiff as I have ever been, but in less than no time I was myself again, and could not have felt more at ease if I had been seeing her for the hundredth time. After the opening compliments, we had a very pleasant and interesting conversation. I stick to my old opinion: we should leave preaching to the ladies. They would make more conversions in one day than the most eloquent missionary could even begin in a lifetime. There is not a man who would not mistake his secret hope of pleasing the preacher for an impulse of grace.

She promised me her portait, and when I left her she gave me her hand to kiss with a gracious air that I cannot describe to you.

From the Rue Garancière I dragged myself to the Quai Bourbon, where I had arranged to meet Damilaville. We had dinner. Drinking with ice seems to have been very good for me; I didn't have the slightest pain in my intestines, and we were able to read a huge article which he had promised me for the Encyclopedia without any interruption.[4]

Tomorrow perhaps, my dear; tomorrow will be Thursday and I shall be feeling well, well enough to regret your absence.

I am writing to you from Le Breton's; I came to check the proofs, which I leave here. I shan't be coming much longer to

[1] Jean-Rodolphe Perronet, architect and Chief Engineer of France, was another of Madame Le Gendre's unfortunate suitors.

[2] The painter Philibert-Benoît La Rue helped Diderot with his accounts of the Salons.

[3] Diderot had dedicated his play *Le Père de famille* to the Princess of Nassau-Saarbrücken in 1758. Her husband was a lieutenant-general in the French army.

[4] The article entitled 'Vingtième', a discussion of income tax.

this damned workshop, where I have worn out my eyes for a set of ruffians who would not give me so much as a stick to beg with. We have only fourteen more sections to print now; it will be done in eight or ten days. In eight or ten days then I shall see the end of this undertaking, which has occupied me for the last twenty years, which has not made my fortune, far from it, which has several times brought me close to exile or imprisonment, and which has consumed a life that could have been both more useful and more illustrious. If men only had themselves to think of, there would be less sacrificing of talents to necessity. Instead we should resign ourselves to drinking water, eating crusts, and following our genius in a garret. But for a wife and children what is there that we are not willing to do? If I wanted to show them what I have done for them I should not say: 'I have worked thirty years for you', but: 'All my life I have renounced my natural vocation for your sake, and against all my inclination I have chosen to do what you needed rather than what I wanted. That is your real debt to me, although you never give it a thought.'

Yesterday evening I was daring enough to tell Madame Le Gendre that she was taking great pains to make a mere pretty doll of her son. *Do not over-educate* is a maxim particularly suited to boys. You should abandon them a little to their natural impulses. I prefer them to be rough, thoughtless, and wilful. I like a tousled head better than a neatly combed one. Let them have the sort of appearance that suits them. If in their foolish behaviour I see some sign of originality, I am satisfied. To my mind one of our unlicked provincial bear-cubs is worth a hundred of your little well-trained spaniels. When I see a boy who listens to himself talking and holds his head up properly and walks correctly and is afraid of getting a hair out of place or a crease in his clothes, the parents may be in raptures and say: 'What a dear little boy we have!', but I say: 'He will never be anything but a fool.'

D'Alembert is in a critical state. He had terrible indigestion and sent for Bouvart, who bled him. I gather that he is in agonies with a colic which threatens to finish him off at any moment. If he dies we shall have lost two great painters and two great mathematicians in three months. Men of his stature are rare and a nation can soon find itself impoverished.

I am writing to you this evening because our presses will be working tomorrow, in spite of the apostles whose day it is, and I shall have double the work to do. It would be very annoying if something held us up on the last page.

There are rumours that Monsieur de Saint-Florentin[1] is going to be replaced by Monsieur de Sartine, who would be replaced by Monsieur Lenoir. And who can tell how Monsieur Lenoir would deal with us? There may not be a grain of truth in any of these supposed changes. But just in case, we are making haste to avoid the difficulties they might cause us.

Goodbye, my dear. Keep well. I know that you love me with all your soul, and you can be sure that I do not lag behind. It is the only one of my debts that I pay in full.

So you hope that it will not be an age until we see one another again? That will largely depend on Monsieur Le Gendre. We are waiting quite patiently for him. The inauguration ceremony has been fixed for the nineteenth of next month;[2] so you can expect dear sister on the ninth or the tenth. I shall be left by myself then. Who shall I have to talk about you with? Who shall I have to go to with this soul full of tender feelings? Where shall I be able to pour out these feelings? Shall I no longer hear the name which is so dear to me, except when I utter it in my unhappiness?

Goodbye, my dear. Goodnight. I am left without paper and without light at the same time. My respects, my loving and sincere respects to your mother. Embrace your sister for me. Tell Miss Mélanie that it would be very bad of her to forget me.

Gaschon has been lanced in the buttocks and they say he is feeling better for it.

## 28

*Paris, 1 August 1765*

Heaven be praised, that's four that have got there! There

[1] Louis Phélypeaux, Comte de Saint-Florentin, had been a Secretary of State since 1736; he had some of the functions of a modern Minister for Cultural Affairs and a Minister of Information.

[2] This inauguration ceremony was for the statue of Louis XV by Pigalle, erected in a square designed by Monsieur Le Gendre at Reims.

are three more on their way to you, not counting this one.

Well, I have sent the Baron on his way; he is leaving his wife, his children and his friends for two months without knowing why. I suspect he is bored in spite of all his wealth and happiness. All that he has is worthless without a feeling heart and a well-balanced mind. Run, my friend, run as far as you like; you will never run away from yourself.

I am writing to you from Damilaville's; he is going off to Geneva tomorrow. I very much fear that a few random, ill-chosen pleasures may cost him his life. It is an exorbitant price to pay.

Yesterday was very wearing for someone whose legs are useless and who had to get round every corner of Paris. I had promised the Baron I would dine with him the day before he left and forgotten that Damilaville had picked the same day to say goodbye to his friends. He had reserved the porter's room at the Luxembourg and arranged everything. So I had no choice but to let the Baron down.

The guests were due to meet in the alley of the Carmelites. There were three or four of us sitting on the bench near the gate of the same name, when we heard shouts coming from the entrance courtyard of the monastery. It was a woman who had fainted on coming out of their church. One of us hurried across and knocked on the monastery door. It was opened by the porter: 'Quickly, Father, bring a drop of your melissa cordial. There is woman here dying.' The monk replied coldly: 'We have no cordial', and shut the door.

I leave it to you to reflect on this example of the powerful effects of religion. There was a monk of another order sitting with us. 'There', he exclaimed sorrowfully, 'that is how a single rude and boorish porter can bring a whole house into disrepute!' 'Never fear, sir', I said. 'What we have just seen is so atrocious that if any of us tried to tell the story, he would be accused of slander.'

This second monk was a fine fellow with a sharp turn of wit, not at all monkish. We talked about paternal love. I told him that it was one of the strongest emotions a man can feel. 'A father's heart', I went on. 'No, really only those who have been fathers can know what that means. It is a secret which luckily even children do not know.' And I added. 'My first years in

Paris were very dissolute. My disorderly conduct was more than enough to make my father angry, even if it had not been exaggerated by slander, as inevitably it was. He had been told. . . . What hadn't he been told? One day I had the opportunity of going and seeing him. I did not hesitate for a moment. Full of confidence in his kindness, I set out for home. I said to myself that when he saw me and I threw myself into his arms, we should weep together and all would be forgiven. And I was not mistaken.' Then I stopped and asked my monk if he knew how far it was from Paris to my home town. 'Sixty leagues, father; and if it had been a hundred, do you think my father would have been any less loving and indulgent?' 'On the contrary.' 'And what if it had been a thousand leagues?' 'How could he possibly deal harshly with a child who had come so far?' 'And what if he had been in the moon, or on Jupiter or Saturn?' As I said these last words, I looked up to heaven and my monk meditated on my parable with his eyes to the ground.

We were in high spirits at dinner. We made so bold as to talk about the bad effect on society of celibacy, without our monk taking offence. He was not particularly hot in defence of the drawbacks of his condition. All he asked was that we should spare those who remain unmarried because of their religion until we had rid the state of those who do so out of profligacy and self-indulgence. We pointed out that the latter do not take vows, that we would forgive the former if they would relinquish theirs and that there was a difference between a bad citizen and someone who swore at the altar to be one. He took it all very well.

You may or may not know that the Benedictines have asked to be secularized in a petition to the King, which has since been printed and published; but you will never believe that the minister was foolish enough not to take them at their word. Yet that is what happened. If every monk had been given a decent pension, there would still have been a huge fortune left, enough to pay off a good part of the nation's debts; this example would have prompted the Carmelites and the Augustinians to ask to be released from their vows, and in less than twenty years, without any violence at all, France would have been rid of the vermin who prey on her and will go on preying on her until they have killed her. Our monk made the shrewd remark that nothing could be more shocking than to say, as the Benedictines had said in their petition, that they asked to be divested of a dishonoured robe, since only misconduct could dishonour the robe and this meant that they were confessing their misconduct.

After dinner we took a stroll. As we walked, my monk asked me why it was that a man seemed to forget his self-love when he heard tell of a good deed, and where the secret joy came from that he felt in spite of himself. I replied that he put himself in the place of either the author or the recipient of the good deed, that when we did not feel able to perform a great action, we took the course of showing that we appreciated its value, and being incapable of generosity, we had to fall back on our sense of justice. I added that it was not always true that we enjoyed hearing about a fine action. Place yourself between a hard-hearted rich man and his poor friend, tell some story of kind, helpful friendship and watch their faces. People do not like lessons which they do not feel capable of following.

At six in the evening the party broke up and I was left alone with Damilaville. Talking about the various eulogies of Descartes which had been presented to the Academy, I made two remarks about eloquence which greatly pleased him. The first was that you should only appeal to the passions when you have persuaded the reason, and that pathos was worthless if the way was not prepared by logic. The second was that when I had been deeply moved by a speaker, I could not bear having this pleasant state of mind interrupted by something violent, and that moments of pathos needed to be followed by something vague and not too insistent, something that did not demand too much concentration; that after strong emotions the orator was exhausted and needed to rest, and so did we.

This conversation which I am making you a party to lasted until eight o'clock, when we separated, he to pack and I to say goodbye to the Baron. I found a whole crowd of his acquaintances gathered at the Rue Royale. We had supper. The Baroness seemed to me to be taking her husband's departure very well, and I thought one could forgive a man for travelling when his wife was so unaffected. I meanwhile had an anxious look on my face; I thought I should have been less concerned if I could have kept him within reach of my eyes and arms, so as to be able to protect him and help him even in the remotest parts of England.

Destiny lies in wait for us everywhere, but we seem to fear it less in places where it has not yet harmed us; we do not know what it has in store for us elsewhere.

If I could see you from here, my dear, if only I had a magic mirror which showed me my love every moment of the day, and if she could walk about in my mirror, before my eyes, as she does at home, then I think I should be easier in my mind. I should hardly let this mirror out of my sight; how often I would get up in the middle of the night to see you sleeping! How often I would cry: 'Be careful, my dear; you are over-tiring yourself; go this way, it is prettier this way. The sun will make you ill; you are staying up too late; you read too much. Don't eat any of that. What is the matter? You look sad.' You wouldn't hear me, but when your reason made you act according to my wishes, I would be as pleased as if you had obeyed me. It is far from certain that my mirror wouldn't cause me more sorrow than joy. It is far from certain that one fine day I wouldn't break it in a fit of temper. But it is certain that having broken it I would pick up all the pieces. What if I happened to see someone kissing your hand in it, if I saw you smiling, if I thought that you were forgetting me too much and for too long at a time! No, no, they can keep their magic mirror; I don't want anything to do with it. My imagination serves us both far better.

It was after midnight when I left the Baron's. Even so I went round to Grimm's place to collect my love's ninth letter. A little German count who has taken a liking to me came with us and put me down at my door at one in the morning. I read you before going to sleep. How could I have slept properly with a sealed letter from my love under my pillow?

Today I have been to see d'Alembert, who has had himself moved from his own house to Watelet's. I found him alone; we had a very affectionate talk. From there I went on to have dinner with our most charming sister and La Rue. After dinner we were to have gone together to see the paintings at the Luxembourg, but the urgent demands of the workshop prevented us.

We continue to have delightful conversations. We talk continually of the mother and the children and grandchildren, since they are what we love most in the whole world; don't forget to tell them this.

Dear sister has had a great adventure. I shall know about it tomorrow; but hush! Goodbye, my love.

## 29

*Paris, 15 September 1765*

This is my number 20, I think. I shall reply on Thursday to your number 22.

Where shall I begin? Upon my word, I have no idea. Why not with our evening talks; for her and for me alike they are delightful hours, to which we look forward all day, and which make her forget her boredom. Why cannot you be there too? Then you would have heard all we say and you would know all the things to which I cannot do justice in writing.

No, there cannot be a more virtuous and innocent creature anywhere than our little sister. At her age, with all her shrewd intelligence and experience as a wife and mother, she is quite blind to anything reprehensible in the manners and conventions of society. She is still a girl of fifteen, it is all a foreign language to her, and the most ordinary things are enigmas whose meaning she can hardly bring herself to believe even when they have been explained to her.

I was telling her that once a man has said: 'I love you' to a married woman and she has replied: 'I love you too', everything is settled and they only have to wait for an opportunity; that if he happens to find her sad, unwelcoming, indifferent, or worried the next day, he presumes that second thoughts and fears have stopped her and made her go back on her formal promise; that the same is true of a girl and a married man and of a man, married or unmarried, and a nun; that there is not a single married woman who does not mean exactly the same by 'I love you' as her lover; that this expression does not carry quite the same weight between a girl and a young man, because it does not reveal a forbidden love, there being still a lawful way of satisfying their mutual desires and the significance of their words being tacitly limited by the will of their parents and a host of other unspoken considerations, whereas those who are separated by the ties of solemn vows are considered to have decided to break them once they confess their love to one another.

She was amazed at all this. When she says to a man: 'I love you', do you know what she means? 'I will only accept from you the qualities my husband lacks, and he is not impotent.' And having thought this out, she was delighted with herself. She genuinely believed that she had laid bare the secret of her heart. It is true that I was unkind enough to rob her of this illusion. 'But if that is so', I said, 'why do you need a lover? Do not I who am your friend and your sister who loves you so dearly offer you together or separately the qualities which your husband lacks?'

And then I gradually brought her to recognize that what she really wants is something more than she said; that there are caresses which she would never receive from either of us and which she would not be averse to, and she admitted it; that if there were a man whom she could trust to remain within certain limits, she would like to sit on his knees, feel his loving arms around her, see the light of passion in his eyes, and put her lips to his forehead, his eyes, his cheeks, and even his lips, and she admitted it; that after putting this lover's self-control to the test a few times, she might one day feel daring enough to give herself over entirely to the intoxication of her heart and senses, and she admitted that too. But what I prophesied to her, and what she will neither admit nor completely deny, is that one day she would feel that she could be happier, that however great the pleasure she had experienced it would come to seem incomplete, that this self-control which she had so solemnly demanded and which he had observed so scrupulously and in such difficult circumstances would come to offend her, that the more virtuous she was, the more she would resent being abandoned by her lover to the relentless struggle of passion against virtue, that afterwards she would be cross with him without knowing the reason why, but that if she took the trouble to examine closely her secret feelings, she would see that while she might praise her lover for keeping his promise so faithfully, she would be extremely vexed with him for not breaking it at a time when her inability to master her feelings, her involuntary weakness, and the treachery of her senses would have been enough to excuse her in her own eyes. And can vanity forgive such a good memory? Can you pardon a man for showing such restraint, when you have completely abandoned yourself? Does he love you enough if he behaves this way? Does he admire your beauty as he ought? I swear that if I know anything about women, there is not one of them who would not break with such a discreet lover sooner or later—and this on the pretext that the pleasures which they had been enjoying together were after all not completely innocent. The lady would feel remorse for exposing herself to danger without any hope of succumbing. She would grow tired of a man who never did of his own accord what she wanted him to do, without daring to admit so much to herself, and she would have no difficulty in finding scores of falsely respectable reasons to hide from herself the true reason for this quite unrespectable breach. She would much prefer to have to grieve and weep the morning after, and heap reproaches on him and herself, and listen to his excuses and accept them and throw herself into his arms again; for after the first fall, one knows secretly that things will continue the same way; and one is irritated at having to wait so long to see whether this fall, which will spare one a painful struggle and give one an uninterrupted succession of unmixed pleasures, is going to occur or not.

There, my love, don't you agree that since Crébillon's Fairy Mole[1] there has been no one to match me for amorous hair-splitting?

The Baron is back from England. He went off prejudiced in favour of the country, he had a very warm welcome there and enjoyed excellent health. Even so, he came home discontented: discontented with the country, which he found to be neither as populous nor as well-cultivated as he had been led to expect, discontented with the architecture, which is almost all odd and Gothic, discontented with the gardens, where the affected imitation of nature is worse than the monotonous symmetry of art, discontented with the taste of people who fill their palaces with a jumble of the good, the excellent, the bad and the execrable, discontented with the festivities, which resemble religious ceremonies, discontented with the people, whose faces never show any trust, friendship, gaiety, or sociability, but always seem to say: 'What can you and I possibly have in common?' Discontented with the great, who are gloomy, unfriendly, proud, disdainful, and vain, discontented with the common people, who

[1] A character in *L'Écumoie*, a story by Crébillon *fils*.

are brutal, insolent, and barbaric, discontented with the dinner parties, where everyone is seated according to rank and where formality and ceremony sit by the side of every guest, discontented with tavern meals, where the service is good and quick, but without any attempt to please.

The only thing I have heard him praise is the ease of travelling. He says that there is not a village, even on the side-roads, where you will not find four or five post-chaises and twenty horses ready waiting. He travelled across Kent, which is one of the most fertile provinces of England, and he declares that it cannot be compared with our Flanders. His trip to England has given him a new taste for living in France, and he confessed to us that he was constantly catching himself thinking: Oh Paris, when shall I see you again? Oh my friends, where are you now? You may be frivolous and silly, you French, but you are still a hundred times better than these miserable gloomy pedants. According to him, France is the only country where you can drink champagne and love and laugh and be merry.

He was very funny when he saw his wife looking in the pink of health. 'Really, madam', he said, 'this is scandalous. Is this how you grieve at your husband's absence? There is nothing for it; if my travels are so good for you, I must go away again.'

Yes, my child, the house is bought.[1] Monsieur has given his procuration and Madame is only kept here by uncertainty as to where she should go. Is she to follow her inclination and go to Isle? Or does her husband intend her to go and meet him at Alençon? I suggested a good trick to her, which was to write to him that she was prepared to do whatever he wanted, that if she had to go Isle, Monsieur Perronet, who had to visit Lorraine, would be happy to keep her company, and that if she had to go to Alençon, Monsieur Perronet, who had to visit the outlying areas of his district, would be happy to postpone his trip to Lorraine. I should have liked to see on which road he preferred to risk being cuckolded.

I had dinner yesterday with a whole colony of English people. They all seemed to have left their pride and melancholy on the banks of the Thames. The Baron did not fail to go and see our friend Garrick and the beautiful mausoleum he has erected in his garden to the spirit of Shakespeare. And it is indeed a beautiful

[1] Monsieur Le Gendre was buying a Paris house in the Rue Sainte-Anne.

mausoleum, and the actor's garden is a beautiful garden. Shakespeare was made for Garrick and Garrick for Shakespeare.

Today I had dinner with a charming woman who is a mere eighty years old, d'Alainville's mother. She is brimming with health and happiness. She still has a tender, loving heart. She speaks of love and friendship with all the vigour and warmth and sensibility of a woman of twenty. There were three of us dining with her, all men. She said to us: 'My friends, a delicate conversation, a look filled with true passion, a tear, an expression of emotion, these are the good things in life. The rest is hardly worth talking about. There are words that were said to me when I was young and that I still remember today, a single one of which is better than ten great exploits. Upon my soul, I think that if I heard them again now, even at my age, my old heart would beat faster.' 'Your heart has not grown old, madam.' 'No, my child, you are right, it is still young, still only twenty years old. I give thanks to God not for giving me a long life, but for allowing me to remain kind, gentle and loving.' As she said this, she looked most attractive.

Really, this conversation was worth more than all the philosophy and politics we had had with the English. But there was one of them who had a funny story to tell. There was a miser who was attacked by highwaymen. He put his head out of the window and said to the robbers: 'Friends, I am called Such-and-such. If you have ever heard of me, you will know that I prize my gold more highly than my life. Do you think it is worth killing me?' The English highwayman did not kill him and the miser kept his money and his life.

Goodnight, my dear. I am going to spend the rest of the night with you. Spend a moment with me. Mademoiselle Boileau will not believe that I behave myself in your absence. Why this incredulity?

## 30

*Paris, early November 1765*

It is off my hands at last,[1] my love, after two weeks of unremitting labour. Grimm, who is fair in all things, is full of

[1] The *Salon* of 1765.

self-reproach; he feels responsible for the disruption of our correspondence, which he rightly regards as our only consolation; then there is my absence from the synagogue of the Rue Royale, where my friends have been missing me, and finally there is the danger to which, according to him, I was exposing myself by working alone for so long at a stretch and performing the sort of feat which, still according to him, is risky at any age, and all the more so at mine, coming on top of twenty years' work. As for what I have done, it amazes him. He swears in two or three of his letters that no one ever has done or ever will do anything like it, and to be honest I was secretly vain enough to think the same thing.

It is certainly the best thing I have done since I began writing, from whatever angle you look at it, the diversity of tone, the variety of subjects, or the abundance of ideas, which I imagine have never passed through any head but mine. It is a storehouse of humour, sometimes light-hearted, sometimes more forceful. In places it is pure fireside conversation. In others it is the heights of eloquence and philosophy. Sometimes I find myself torn between contradictory feelings. There are times when I wish the whole work could suddenly appear in print in the middle of Paris, but more often, when I think of the pain it would cause a host of artists who do not deserve to be so harshly punished for their ineffectual attempts to win our admiration, I should be very grieved if it were to appear. Far be it from me to preserve such a misplaced feeling of vanity, when I think that my work would be enough to take away the reputation and the livelihood of poor artists, who may paint pitifully badly, but who are no longer young enough to change their profession and have a wife and a brood of children to support. Remembering this, I keep from the light a production which could easily bring me fame and fortune. This is yet another source of regret for Grimm, to see something hidden away in his shop, as he calls it, when it certainly does not appear to have been meant to remain unknown.

This undertaking has been a pleasant source of satisfaction to me. I have proved to myself that I still have the fire and imagination I had when I was thirty, together with a wealth of knowledge and judgement which I did not have then. I took up my pen and wrote for two weeks without stopping, from morning to night. I filled more than two hundred pages with ideas and style, two hundred pages of the size I use for my letters and in the same small writing; it would make approximately two good printed volumes. I have also discovered that my vanity can do without popular applause, and even that I do not mind much whether or not I am appreciated by those I see regularly, so long as there is one man in the world whose judgement I respect and who knows my value.

Grimm knows it, and perhaps he has never known it as well as he does now! It is also pleasant for me to think that I have given a few moments' amusement to my Russian benefactress, dealt a few blows to fanaticism and prejudice, and given a few lessons in passing to the rulers of the nations; not that they will act any the better for it, but they will not have the excuse of not having heard the truth, and the naked truth at that. From time to time I apostrophize them as perpetrators of unhappiness and falsehood, and dealers in hope and fear.

My long period of retreat intrigued Gaschon; he bestirred himself to come round to my house. He arrived at the same time as Monsieur Le Gendre. You will be seeing the latter very soon. As for me, I shall appear to you when your solitude is complete and you are kept indoors by the bad weather. I shall come with the ice, the snow, and the frost.

Goodbye, my dear. Keep in good health. Give my respects to your mother and all her children and grandchildren. I love you with all my heart, and your sister too.

However you interpret this last line, it remains true. Goodbye, goodbye.

## 31

*Paris, 20 December 1765*

One task follows another, and I am beginning to fear that the thought of rest is nothing but a mirage. The day before yesterday I had on my desk a comedy, a tragedy, a translation, a political work and a lawyer's brief, not to mention a comic opera.

The comic opera is by Marmontel;[1] it is a dramatic version

[1] Jean-François Marmontel (1723–99) was a member of the Academy, author of the *Contes moraux* and subsequently of some famous memoirs.

which he has made of his story *The Shepherdess of the Alps.* It was sent to me for my opinion, and my opinion is that it is an unpromising subject and that barring a miracle from the composer, it will be a failure. The Baroness does not know where she stands in this affair; she does not care for the poet, but she is very attached to the composer. He is Kohaut, her lute teacher, the one who gave Madame Le Gendre and Mélanie such a pleasant evening. When I got there yesterday the author and the musician were quarrelling; 'Don't be in such a hurry, my friends', I said; 'wait until after the first performance.'

The comedy is by one of those young men from Marseille whom friend Gaschon introduced to me. It is poor stuff and the worst of it is that it does not give promise of anything better.

The tragedy is by a young man who is a great admirer of *The Siege of Calais*[1] and whom I have had all the trouble in the world persuading that the age of recognition scenes and conspiracies is past and that it is almost as difficult today to find a worthwhile, interesting, new subject as to treat it well.

The translation is Abbé Le Monnier's version of Terence. To be honest, I do not know when I shall have finished with the poor Abbé; we are more afraid of offending strangers than friends, so friends are always the last to be served.

The political work is by poor Abbé Raynal[2] whom I have been driving mad with impatience and boredom for the last six months.

And the brief, to which I would happily give all my time and skill, because the cause is worth the trouble, is by a Scot called Stuart, who is fighting for a great title and an inheritance of several millions against a child who was set up to replace the true heir by parents afflicted with posteromania.[3] This cause is almost as much the mathematician's province as the lawyer's. It would be the ideal place for someone who knew his probability calculus to exercise his talents. If the affair concerned me, I should ascertain the degree of probability which in a judge's eyes justifies condemning a man to death, and I do not think I should have a hard task in showing that there is a greater probability

[1] *Le Siège de Calais*, a patriotic drama by De Belloy, produced in 1765.

[2] The *Histoire des Deux Indes*, an important work on colonialism to which Diderot contributed a great deal.

[3] Stuart's brief concerned the famous Douglas case which had begun in 1761 and lasted for several years.

that the child in question is not the true heir. Whence I should conclude against the judges that it would be monstrous to demand stronger proof for depriving a man of his title and his fortune than for depriving him of his honour and his life.

I do not know if you were still in Paris when I was summoned to Monsieur d'Outremont's to decide whether certain letters which had been produced as evidence in this case were genuine or forged. I have re-read these letters and it is crystal clear to me that they were written not by a Frenchman, but by a foreigner, that this foreigner was an Englishman and that this Englishman was the child's supposed father, who wrote them under the name of a midwife. As you see, I am keeping to my plan of telling you about every minute of my life.

Today Friday, the eve of St. Thomas's day, we have lost Monsieur le Dauphin, after a long and painful illness which he endured with truly heroic patience. There are innumerable accounts of his noble words and actions. They say that a little while ago he cut off his hair and shared it between his sisters saying it was the only present he could give them. There is something touching and reminiscent of the Ancients about this action which makes it extremely beautiful in my eyes. A great nobleman wrote him a quite ridiculous letter, begging him to ask the King for a favour, which he said he was bound to grant him, since the Dauphin was in a state in which he could refuse him nothing. The Dauphin made a joke of this impertinence, but did not name the letter-writer.

Throughout his illness he had the delicacy to appear to those around him far less concerned for his health and his life than he can possibly have been. The only time when he seemed attached to his life was when he received from his father a mark of affection which touched him. Monsieur Hume, who had it from Monsieur de Nivernois, told me that a few months ago, when the duke went to pay his respects to the Dauphin, he found him in bed reading the philosophical works of Hume, which you no doubt know and which are not famous for their orthodoxy. The duke was surprised, and no doubt doubly surprised if the Dauphin added, as Monsieur Hume told me he did, that this book was very comforting in the state he was in.

It is certain that the Dauphin had read widely and thought deeply, and that there were few important subjects on which he was not very well informed. Some of the things he said prove that he could also be quite flippant and witty. They say that shortly before his death, having heard that Rousseau of Geneva was not being allowed to settle in Strasbourg, he expressed disapproval of this severity, even though he was in no doubt that circumstances justified it, and declared that he was a man deserving pity rather than persecution. These are certainly not the words of an intolerant man.

Rousseau has been in Paris for three days now. I don't expect a visit from him, but I will not deny that it would give me great pleasure and that I should be very interested to see how he would justify his behaviour towards me.[1] It is just as well that I am not too open in my affections; when once I have let someone in, it tears my heart to let him out again, and the wound never heals over completely.

Some time ago I came across a letter of his, which contained some delightful things. Talking of priests, he said that they had set themselves up as the judges of scandal, stirred up scandal and then as a result of this scandal hauled men before their tribunals to be punished for the crime which they themselves had committed. What an infallible method, he went on, for harassing private individuals, society, subjects, magistrates, monarchs, entire nations and the whole world at will. Then he compared them to the surgeon who lived at a cross-roads, so that his shop had doors on to two streets. This surgeon went out by one door and wounded passers-by; then he ran back in and appeared at the other door to dress their wounds—the only slight difference being that the man at the cross-roads did in fact cure the harm he had done, whereas the priest only hurries to make it worse.

Rousseau will spend a fortnight here. He is waiting to travel with Monsieur Hume, who will take him to England and install him at Pelham, a little village on the Thames, where he will be able to live in peace, if it is really peace that he wants. Monsieur de Saint-Lambert made a delightful remark about him: 'Do not pity him too much; he is travelling with his mistress, Reputation.'

At this moment, you are by yourself with mama, acting out the fable of the pigeon who stayed at home and the pigeon who went on his travels.[6] Where are they now? The roads are very

[1] As far as we know, Rousseau and Diderot never met again.
[2] See La Fontaine's fable, 'Les Deux Pigeons'.

bad. They will have suffered a lot from the cold. Mademoiselle Mélanie will arrive a week too late to hear the panteleon.[1]

I was very glad to hear from you that I can go and see dear sister without the risk of meeting Mademoiselle Boileau. I fear her like the plague. I owe her an apology, but this embarrasses me more than it worries me.

However much that poor little sister gets hurt she never gets used to it. It is a sad state of affairs. What is worse is that when everyone else gets tired of hurting her, she goes and hurts herself.

You flatter me on my perspicacity. When one has some slight experience in reading what is in one's own heart, one becomes very knowledgeable about what is going on in other people's. What a lot of plausible pretexts I have taken for valid reasons in my time! This assiduous self-scrutiny serves less to make us better ourselves than to teach us that neither we nor anyone else is any too virtuous. Shall I give you the last word on little sister? Her only hope is in the decayed state of the man in question. Little sister is a bird, and he is not of an age to go shooting at birds on the wing.

That reminds me of a droll remark made by a certain woman, though Uranie would never say the same thing to her suitor. A man was being very pressing, and this woman suspected that he was not the man he would have her believe. So she said to him: 'Be careful, Sir; I shall take you at your word.' After the age of fifty there is hardly one of us who would not be embarrassed by this frankness. Try it some time and you will see. I don't include priests and monks however, as they have the grace attached to their profession.

But why didn't little sister agree to perform that unpleasant task? That was a mistake on her part.

Please don't tell me what mama will or will not do. I swear that she has no idea herself, and that in her place I should be just the same. I see that when it is a choice between harming oneself and harming others, good people always end up by giving themselves the preference. But why do you go reading to others what I only wrote for you? At one time it was feared that this confidence would put me on too good terms with the niece, but

[1] In another letter Diderot describes this instrument as 'a sort of dulcimer, four feet wide and nine feet long, with seventy-four different notes.'

my fear is that one day it may put me on very bad terms with the aunts. I want neither the one nor the other. You have grown very cautious; don't you find it burdensome to restrain yourself?

I keep saying to myself, and then scolding myself for saying it: 'What! am I to go on letting a mere Dom Diego[1] treat me like a fool for a whole month, without so much as hinting to him that it is he who is the fool? It's too much to bear.'

I have not seen much of Mademoiselle Boileau, but I have made up for it by spending a lot of time with the fable-writing Abbé.

Sedaine's play has been performed and received just as I thought it would be.[2] The first day was a pitched battle: on my left the gentlemen, the artists, and the people of taste, on the right the mob. Don't tell anyone, my dear, but I assure you that the people who are praising the play to the skies at present do not really appreciate its value. It is so subtle, so delicate, so exquisite, so simple, so true! *Piscis hic non est omnium.* I am sure that Saurin, Helvétius, and others feel great pity for the public. It is either true or false, my dear (the play, I mean). If it is false, it is worthless; but if it is true, what a lot of so-called beautiful things are worthless!

Can you tell me whether I have to pay up? I wagered the Abbé that the actors would cut a particular scene, a scene of real genius. The actors did not cut it, but the public did. At the first night I could see quite clearly that of the two thousand spectators I was almost the only one who really appreciated the play's qualities. It calls for a very pure and refined feeling for art. Even today the only people I trust to judge it properly are a few good honest straightforward men and women who were instinctively delighted by it, without knowing why. The Aristotelians are all at sea. Mark my prophecy; Voltaire will not have a good word to say for it.—And what about the court?—They will call it a lot of idle gossip and chatter. Perhaps, but it is the sort of gossip and chatter that Lelius and Scipio were suspected of dictating to Terence, only more lively and less elegant. (No, the other way

[1] A nickname for Monsieur Le Gendre.

[2] *Le Philosophe sans le savoir*, a serious comedy by Michel-Jean Sedaine (1719–97); Sedaine puts into practice many of the ideas for dramatic renewal (blurring of the distinction between comedy and tragedy, natural dialogue, etc.) which Diderot had advocated in the 1750s.

round.) He produces all the terrors of tragedy with what seems like a comic opera. A few days ago, during the last scene but one, a young girl cried out from the middle of the circle: 'Oh! he is dead!' How I wish she had been my daughter! How I would have kissed her, there and then!

*Change myself*?—Yes, every part of me except the lover, whom I shall leave alone. He is excellent as he is. Don't you think so? He is only lacking in one thing; that is being close to the one he loves. And he intends to put that right as soon as possible.

Goodbye, my love. My respects to mama.

## 32

*Paris, 20 September 1767*

Let's see if I can continue my journal. The last lines I wrote were from Mousseau, I think. A funny thing happened on the way back, the sort of slip which you hardly expect, although in fact it is quite natural. We were coming home in the evening in a gig. Bron[1] and I were sitting down inside it and I had on my knees a woman with whom he has been on very good terms for a long time and who for a very long time has been jealous of another woman, whom he claims not to frequent or have any sort of liaison with. We had to go past this woman's door and just as we were getting close, the horse suddenly left the road and shot over towards the house. The driver whipped him up. The horse thought he had turned too sharply and made the movements a horse usually makes when he has come up to the entrance to a house awkwardly and is trying to approach it better. In short, it was the devil's own job to stop him taking us where we certainly had no intention of going. The woman who was sitting on my knees said to my friend, who was sitting next to me: 'You see, your horse is more truthful than you.'

We travelled the rest of the way in silence. I went to the prince's for supper, and he showed me another letter from the fair lady.[2] She is extremely touched by all the kindness you have

[1] Little is known of this friend of Diderot's except that he was a post office official.

[2] Mademoiselle Dornet, a dancer at the Opera and at this time the mistress of Prince Golitsyn, the Russian ambassador.

shown her, and she writes about it in the warmest and sincerest manner imaginable. As for him, he is overjoyed, and I receive the reward for your good deeds; he embraces me, kisses me, and cannot stop thanking me; he has told me to send you his heartfelt gratitude. It was on Monday evening that we had supper together. Since then he has had no word from his lady, and this has made him extremely anxious. My role then is to console him by saying: 'She is on her way, she has people to see; perhaps she is in Metz now, busy cultivating Monsieur d'Estaing and getting her brothers promoted.' Whereupon he gets up in a rage and shouts: 'Curse you, you crazy philosopher, are you set on driving me mad?' Then he calms down and adds: 'Come now, my friend, no more of these bad jokes; does it make you happy to break my heart?' The melancholy Dutch ambassador holds his sides and laughs until the tears run down his cheeks.

Then we discuss the matter seriously. We agree that any woman who is at all attractive and sharp-witted has a hundred chances a month to deceive us without our knowing a thing about it, and that the simplest course, as well as the surest and most reasonable, is to show such confidence in her that she is ashamed to let us down. The prince admits this, but on condition that he is allowed to be suspicious and jealous and that no one makes fun of him.

On Tuesday it was the Salon from half past seven until two or three o'clock; then dinner with the beautiful hostess of the Rue des Poulies, and a stroll until nightfall. At eight o'clock, off to the Rue Sainte-Anne.[1] Her son is making unheard-of progress. Master Digeon came to tell her about it and she was overjoyed, but this was only a passing gleam of sunshine and I found them both sad. But since I owe any further knowledge of their affairs to her confidences rather than to my observation, I cannot tell you anything more. Master Digeon has no liaison with Madame de Grandpré and never has had. She made this discovery when discussing the tutor whom she keeps talking about engaging, but never actually engages. She was saying to him: 'It is becoming an absolute necessity. I am afraid that your assiduity here may upset a person to whom I should hate to cause any unhappiness.' 'I understand what you mean, madam; I swear to you that the

[1] To the house of Madame Le Gendre, who was at this time flirting with her son's tutor, Digeon.

person in question is very interested in the success of my labours and has no reason to disapprove of them.' 'But then another person might come to hear of them.' 'She knows of them already; she and I have been living our own lives for a long time now. When we meet we do not hide anything from one another or reproach one another with anything we have done.' 'But what about society? I have a daughter; if it was thought that you had designs on her, that would be enough to keep away any possible husbands. And if they supposed something else, there are sensible people who would judge the daughter's morals by the mother's and . . .' 'What can I say to that, madam?'

And I say, listening to her account of these conversations: 'I do not know what you have in mind, dear sister, but do you not see that you and he are now on the most intimate footing, that you have authorized Monsieur Digeon to follow your example in touching freely on certain subjects, and that after these indiscreet questions he is quite entitled to discuss any subject he likes with you?' She admits it. 'But what's to be done now?' 'Nothing, except to declare very clearly and unaffectedly, the next time you have a talk of this nature, exactly what you think about the duties of a respectable woman, the danger of liaisons of this kind, the risk of losing one's domestic peace and public reputation, the need for self-respect, and a hundred and one other things which you will express so forcefully that you stop your suitor in his tracks for the next few months at least. I do not know what will happen after that.' 'No more do I.' 'But since we can be sure that Nature will not make an exception to her general laws in your favour, people will notice Monsieur Digeon's inclination whether you encourage it or not, and so your son will have lost the best tutor he could have, your door will be closed to Monsieur Digeon and the boy may have to be shut up in a college. You will just have to make the best of it.'

When I got home on Tuesday evening, there was a note telling me the Baron was in Paris and another one from Grimm saying that he had returned from La Briche with a certain Baron von Schweidnitz, who did not want to go back to Gotha without being able to tell his princess that he had seen me, embraced me and kissed me on her behalf, and that I must come without fail to a picnic the next day, Wednesday, at the lodge by the Porte des Feuillants. This note of Grimm's was peppered with a few bad-tempered remarks which hurt me: namely that I went everywhere except to La Briche, that Madame d'Épinay had been there by herself and had been waiting in vain for me to visit her, that all the thanks she got for her humouring of my tastes and even my whims was to be insultingly neglected. Just think, the only reason I went to Le Grandval was to do the Baron a favour, the only reason I went to Mousseau was because it was convenient for going in to the Salon every morning, and the only reason I stay in Paris is to work on this damned Salon for him. And then the Baron, who does what he pleases and who would have been only too pleased to transact his business in Paris and take me back on Thursday to Le Grandval delivered an abominable tirade against me for disappointing him. It was too much to bear; the injustice of all these people provoked me to an eloquent outburst against friendship. I depicted it as the most unendurable tyranny, the trial of my life, and I concluded: 'Friends, you whom I call friends for the last time, I declare to you that I no longer have any friends, nor do I wish for any, and that I intend to live alone, since I was born under such an evil star that I cannot make anyone happy, when I abandon myself entirely to those I love.'

As I said this, despair seized me and I shed floods of tears; then the Marquis,[1] who was sitting by me, put his arm round me and led me to the other side of the Tuileries, where this scene took place while we were waiting for dinner. He talked to me in the most reasonable, loving, and comforting way and when he brought me back to the friends I had just renounced, I had regained some of my peace of mind and was prepared to dine with them instead of going off home. The thing that had hurt me most was Grimm's saying to me that since he could no longer write to me if he could not tell the truth, and since I found the truth so painful, he would stop writing to me. 'And yet these are the people who pride themselves on their sensibility', I said to the Marquis. 'When I complain about the pain they cause me, they rub it in by saying coolly that they will cause me no more.' Even so, the dinner was very pleasant; we talked about the petty

[1] The Marquis de Croismare was a friend of the *philosophes*; he had a country house at Mousseau (or Mouceaux), near the present site of the Parc Monceau. Probably it was he who was Diderot's host there in 1767.

character of those who are too vain to accept help. We parted early and we embraced one another very affectionately.

Damilaville wanted to take me with him to see Madame de Maux, who is ill and is being bled in the foot. I felt more inclined to go to the Rue Sainte-Anne, which I did. I did not stay long. Madame Le Gendre was planning to go and collect Madame de Blacy[1] from Monsieur de Tressan's and she asked me if I could get her any horses. I went that evening to have supper with the prince; I asked him for horses and he let me have some. The prince and I spent the evening arguing about a principle of painting: that Nature has many masses, but few groups. You will not understand this, but all I need to tell you is that we both appealed to the compositions of the great masters, and that I proved to him that in the compositions of Poussin, which sometimes contain up to a hundred or a hundred and twenty figures, there may be ten, twelve, fifteen or twenty masses, but at most two or three groups, particularly in the *Judgement of Solomon*, which has twenty or thirty figures and not a single group.

The rest of the evening was spent chatting about misalliances entered into without parental consent; in this connection, he told a story about a certain Monsieur de Parceval which you may not know and which you will like. His son married without his consent. The day after the wedding, his daughter-in-law came to see him. He was still in bed. She knelt down by his bed, took one of his hands and watered it with her tears. Monsieur de Parceval said to her: 'But wasn't my son afraid of being disinherited?' His daughter-in-law replied: 'He knows you too well to be afraid of that.' After a moment's silence, Monsieur de Parceval went on: 'Stand up, my child. You have taken a son away from me; I hope that in nine months you will give me another, and that you will bring him up so well that he will never dare to make even a good match without your consent.' Then he kissed her; but he refused to see his son. In order to reconcile father and son, they had recourse to the good offices of Monsieur de Saint-Florentin. Hardly had he broached the subject than the excellent Parceval said to him: 'Oh! your Excellency, what an unhappy time you would have saved me, if only you had thought of doing this sooner!'

[1] This was the name adopted by Madame de Salignac after her husband's scandalous bankruptcy.

All of Thursday went on my negotiations at Sainte-Périne,[1] which are making no progress at all; the night from Thursday to Friday and a good part of Friday I spent at home, writing up my notes on the Salon. I had dinner with the family. I listened to my daughter playing the harpsichord. I was visited by Madame Geoffrin, who treated me like a fool and advised my wife to do the same. Last time she came and corrupted my daughter; this time she would have come and corrupted my wife and taught her to swear and despise her husband, if this had not been her practice already.

I don't know what became of me for the rest of the day. I went and sat for a few minutes with Madame Le Gendre, who informed me that Madame de Blacy had come home and that she herself was going to use the prince's horses to go to Sceaux or on some other country outing that she had arranged with Monsieur Digeon. I smiled; she did her utmost to make me give up my dinner at Mousseau and come with her. When I refused point-blank, she decided to get Madame de Blacy to come, and then it occurred to her that people might think she was afraid of a long *tête-à-tête*, and then she didn't know what she would do. And the next day, which was Saturday, she wrote to me, apropos of a little favour she was asking of me, saying that she had proposed the excursion to Madame de Blacy, who had accepted. So there they were, she, Monsieur Digeon, her children and Madame de Blacy, galloping off to Sceaux, while I was on my way to Mousseau—and it is from Mousseau that I am writing to you now on Sunday morning to tell you that I am going back to Paris to have dinner with her, and after dinner going home quite early in the evening to pack my bag for Le Grandval, where I shall be taken tomorrow, Monday, by the Marquis, Grimm, and Damilaville, and where I shall spend the rest of the month, not that that will prevent me from receiving your letters and posting a few of my own at Boissy.

This detailed account of my life has made me forget a lot of things. The prince's fate is decided. I have had news from Russia. A bust of the Empress is coming for me. Falconet[2] has quarrelled

[1] In an earlier letter Diderot says he has been to Sainte-Périne de Chaillot to persuade a woman 'that it is better to be a good mother than a good lover'.

[2] The sculptor, Étienne-Maurice Falconet, had been invited to Saint Petersburg in 1766 and spent twelve years there working on the equestrian statue of Peter the Great (Pushkin's 'Bronze Horseman'). The manuscript Diderot mentions is an

with General Betzky, but he is such a favourite of the Empress that the ministers have more to fear from him than he from them. He has sent me that manuscript about the feeling of immortality and the respect due to posterity which I was so afraid he would publish in Saint Petersburg without my having a hand in it, and he encloses with his manuscript a note where he repeats the offers I have told you about. You cannot imagine the heart-searching this causes me. It is a cruel tug-of-war between the gratitude I owe the monarch and my love for you. But it is you who will always win, my love. Yes, I am capable of taking the pile of gold I have received and throwing it at the ambassador's feet, but I am not capable of leaving you. Goodbye, my dear. Don't scold me; don't join with my friends in poisoning my life. I greet you and embrace you with all my heart. Give my loving respects and my undying devotion to mama. Take care of her health, and may she take care of yours. Hurry back to Paris. What lovely weather we are having! What lovely walks we could still have at Meudon, if you wished!

Goodbye, goodbye. I hope Damilaville will hand me a letter from you when he countersigns this one of mine.

* * *

It is strange, though, isn't it, how wrong we can be in our judgement of things and how often our high hopes of them are disappointed? Almost overnight I saw my fortune doubled, my daughter's dowry made up without any sacrifice of my modest income and myself assured of comfort and wealth for the rest of my days; I rejoiced at this and you rejoiced with me. And what have I gained by it so far? What has it really done for me? This gift from an empress forced me to borrow money. The loan reduced my small income; the new use I am making of my capital, which was already depleted by the money I received in advance, led to another loan; and in this way, without any extravagance on my part, a series of payments could completely drain my funds without my ever being any the richer.

The whole business is very funny, but it is not at all funny that in order to show my gratitude to my benefactress I am more or less obliged to undertake a journey of seven or eight hundred

exchange of letters between them, subsequently published under the title *Le Pour et le contre*.

leagues. If I don't do this. I shall blame myself, and shall perhaps be held to blame by her. All these ideas keep tormenting me. Come back to Paris then, and let me forget all my duties and my troubles by your side. Falconet, who has had my letter from Monsieur de la Rivière, tells me that it is written in exactly the same style as the letters from the corner of the Rue Taranne to the Rue d'Anjou, and that even so he is constantly tempted to send it to the Empress. He will succumb eventually, take my word for it, and as you know, that is just what I intended when I wrote it. Well then, what will the Empress see in it? She will see that I am in love, madly in love, and that all her gifts are nothing compared with the happiness of my beloved. She will see that what keeps me here is what has always led men to great exploits, great crimes and acts of folly both great and small, and that when you are in love you are both as good and as bad as you could possibly be. If she is capable of true thought and feeling, she will not say: 'He is ungrateful', but: 'He is in love.' Believe me, she has already seen my letter and has forgiven me—or so I like to think, for my own peace of mind.

But you must return to Paris. When I see you, all will be well, and even if it is not I shall not care. I remember having said once that someone had no more morals than you would find in the head of a pike. I have changed my comparison; now I should say 'than in the heart of a lover'. The true lover is a lover and nothing else. It is too bad for honesty and virtue if they find themselves in the way of love. Not that love would lead us to do anything despicable or degrading; we would not steal a few coins for love, but we would commit arson and murder and suicide.

Goodbye, goodbye; they said they would wake me early and take me back to Paris at nine in the morning, but they went off without me. Now they are planning to keep me here for dinner, and I fear they will succeed. If that happens I shall be late getting back to Paris, but nothing will prevent me from going to see Madame de Blacy; I absolutely must have a word with her about her son. Perhaps she will have seen the man who brought her the pitiful letters she had from him. Before I see Monsieur Dubucq, I must know whether he is innocent or guilty; the answer will determine what tone I adopt.[1]

[1] Madame de Blacy's son Vallet de Fayolle had just been the victim (or the cause)

Shall I not hear in your next letter when you will be coming back?

Goodbye once again. If you do not love me, take care.

The prince has packed his bags.

Decipher this scribble if you can.[1]

33

*Paris, 3 October 1767*

My little girl is playing her instrument divinely, but I am leaving her to chat with you. Here I am then, home from Le Grandval, very much against the will of the Baron, the Baroness, the little boys and girls, Madame d'Aine, and the servants. I have abandoned them all to the bad temper of a master who takes pleasure in tormenting his family when he has not got a friend to make him happy. I am hunting about and writing in all directions to find someone to go to the rescue. But Galiani likes the town where he can constantly be performing. Doctor Gatti is Madame de Choiseul's shadow. D'Alainville is distributing accommodation at Fontainebleau. Grimm is at La Briche, doing the correct thing and getting bored. When Morellet[2] is not at Voré, he is on the way there. The fair Madame Helvétius keeps him on his toes. Our Orpheus[3] is at L'Isle-Adam. Suard is dancing attendance on so many women that he can hardly spare a thought for the Baroness.

I have harangued Monsieur Le Romain[4] in vain; they would be very glad to see him, but he prefers to stay in his dark cabin, distilling blackness to smear over the face of nature, rather than

---

of a disastrous fire in French Guiana. Dubucq was an important official in the colonial administration and helped Fayolle in his career.

[1] Other editors have dated the final section of this letter about two months later than the rest. It is, however, written on the same piece of paper and its contents suggest that it was composed on the Sunday when Diderot's friends had failed to wake him and take him back from Mousseau to Paris.

[2] Abbé André Morellet (1727–1819), friend of the *philosophes* and author of various works on economics and politics, and of two volumes of memoirs.

[3] The lute-player Kohaut.

[4] An engineer and contributor to the *Encyclopédie*.

enjoying the charms of the country. It would not be difficult to tempt fat Berger, but they are not interested, since he is gloomy, silent, sleepy, and unreliable. Damilaville always has the pretext of his work, not that he ever does any. Naigeon[1] would die of boredom if he could not go regularly to the Vanloos' where he is sure of finding Madame Blondel, whom he does not love but talks about continually, and if he did not have his daily walk in the Palais-Royal at precisely the same time as her.

Abbé Raynal does not feel at home if he cannot lecture about colonies, politics, and trade. Monsieur de Saint-Lambert is chained to Montmorency. Young d'Aine is hot in pursuit of the post of administrator at Auch, which he affects to despise as the fox despised sour grapes. The Baron von Gleichen would sooner have the excavations at Herculaneum than the most beautiful gardens in the world. Friend Le Roy lives only for himself; he never goes anywhere unless he hopes to amuse himself more there than elsewhere; and in any case it is the season for hunting, which is his passion. Croismare needs variety too much to stay in one place more than one day; he has never packed up his nightcap and lost sight of the Quai de la Ferraille, the booksellers and the picture-dealers without the strongest and most respectable of motives.

Women would be easy to find, but they are not wanted since so few of them are men. Doctor Roux is looking for patients. Doctor James is still chasing his horse. Doctor Darcet is perhaps being kept under lock and key by the Comte de Lauraguais until he has made a discovery for him. Count Creutz[2] is in ecstasies in front of his paintings or in front of the painter's wife, who is pretty and very flirtatious. Helvétius, with his bonnet on his head, is busy on his estate analysing sentences and proving that his kennelman could have written his *Essays on the Mind* as well as he. Wilkes[3] is no longer in favour, because he is on the verge of ruin and without noticing it we meet misfortune half-way and break off relations before it happens, since it would not be right to do so afterwards. The Chevalier de Chastellux is tied up somewhere and when you are young that sort of knot is hard to untie.

[1] Jacques-André Naigeon (1738–1810), maliciously called 'Diderot's ape', later helped in the first publication of many of his works.
[2] The Swedish ambassador in Paris.
[3] The English politician, John Wilkes.

The Baroness says that Abbé Coyer is like Narbonne honey that has gone off, so I am not to send him to her. The Chevalier de Valori has been turning a deaf ear for close on sixty years. And that is almost the whole circle; you know them nearly as well as I do. Given this famine, I have just sent them Berlize the Jew, who is young d'Aine's secretary and his mother's estate manager. He acts the fool and talks nonsense; everyone laughs at him, he gets cross and they laugh all the more.

My return to Paris was delayed three or four days, thanks to a crafty trick of the Baroness who secretly corrupted everyone who had agreed to come and fetch me home. I arrived just in time to deal with the aftermath of a series of little domestic storms which had arisen in my absence between the two sisters, the mother and daughter, and the aunt and niece. They each came to tell me their grievances; they were all in the wrong and I told them all they were in the right. The little doll has agreed to be more careful what she says and peace reigns again. My first thought on arriving was to go and see Madame de Blacy, for much as I love to laugh, I love consoling those who weep even more.

Then I paid a visit to little sister, whom I found reading your letters and nodding her head at every protestation of friendship. Monsieur Digeon was there. I was invited to dinner for today, Saturday, but we remembered that that day had been promised to the country-dwellers of Mousseau, and this started us talking about the sacredness of promises. Our dear sister was reeling out a whole series of splendid maxims on the subject, when I took the liberty of remarking that there are scores of different ways of promising which are just as binding as the most explicit declaration or a letter signed in blood. 'For example', I added, 'there are favours which my friend has never actually promised me, but which I count on as a part of the pact of friendship; and when I have occasion to ask for them, I refer to them as if they had been promised me at the moment when the word "friend" was first spoken between us.'

And so we were off on the duties attached to friendship. On this question I stuck to La Fontaine's fable;[1] I thought that my friend should be roused from his bed by the mere suspicion that I might not be sleeping well, and that he should offer me his

[1] 'Les Deux Amis', which begins: 'Two true friends lived in Monomotapa'.

slave-girl, if I did not want to sleep alone. Monsieur Digeon shook his head at the slave-girl, but I told him that was because I was from Monomotapa and he was not.

We changed the subject and talked about my long stay in the country and the sort of life we led at Le Grandval. I was asked if the Baroness was really happy. I replied with the truth, namely that she is happy wherever the Baron is contented and she has her children and her lute. To understand what follows you need to know that Madame Le Gendre has perhaps seen Suard two or three times at Madame de Grandpré's and that Suard has been a friend of Monsieur Digeon and Madame de Grandpré for the last fifteen years.

Talking of the difference between the life the Baroness leads at Le Grandval and the life she leads in Paris, I observed that it is to her credit that the town pleasures which she most enjoys are sacrificed as soon as ever she notices on her husband's face that he does not completely approve of them. As I said this, I saw Monsieur Digeon and Madame Le Gendre smiling at one another. This displeased me. Monsieur Digeon went off to give the young gentleman his lesson. I remained alone with her and Madame de Blacy, whereupon I adopted a much more decided and serious tone than usual and said to Madame Le Gendre that those who only knew Madame d'Holbach by what Suard said, did not know her at all, since Suard was not the man to speak well of her.

I surmised, and correctly I think, that Suard had been inconsiderate enough to disparage the Baroness to his friend, and that this friend had thoughtlessly passed on the mistaken idea he had been given to Madame Le Gendre. After a few minutes' silence Madame Le Gendre lit her candle and left the room, and this finally confirmed my suspicions. I guessed that she had gone to pass on my outburst to Monsieur Digeon while it was still hot from the press—and I am sure I was right. And these are the people they call gentlemen! They are admitted to a house, the master of the house heaps kindness and favours on them, comes to regard them highly and to consider them his friends and gives them every possible mark of his feelings towards them, and in return they do all they can to seduce his wife and, when they fail, to ruin her reputation. If Monsieur Digeon continues like this he will fall a long way in my estimation. He sees only the black side of humanity. He has no faith in virtuous actions; he belittles them and casts doubt on them. If he tells a story, it is always a shocking and scandalous one. That is the second woman of my acquaintance he has spoken about to Madame Le Gendre; he has maligned both of them. Of course they have their failings, but they have good qualities. Why keep quiet about the good qualities and dwell on the failings? This reveals a kind of envy which offends me, for I read men as I read books, remembering only what is worth knowing and imitating.

The conversation between Suard and Madame de Grandpré and Madame le Gendre had been very heated as a result of a mistake made by Madame Le Gendre. They had been searching for the reason why sensitive souls are so quickly, strongly, and agreeably affected by stories of noble actions. Suard had asserted that it was because of a sixth sense which Nature gave us to judge the good and the beautiful. They asked me what I thought. I replied that this sixth sense, which a few metaphysicians have brought into fashion in England, is a figment of the imagination; that all our ideas come from experience; that we learn from our earliest years what it is in our interest to conceal or reveal; that when we are conscious of the motives for our actions, judgements and proofs, we are said to have knowledge of them; that when we cannot remember them we are said to possess taste, instinct, or flair; that the reasons for showing that stories of noble actions move us are innumerable; that we reveal that we possess admirable qualities; that we promise our admiration to others if ever they deserve it by unusually virtuous actions; that hearing of noble actions makes us hope to meet with someone capable of performing them among our acquaintance, that by our extreme admiration of them we suggest to others that we should be capable of performing them if the opportunity arose; that apart from all these selfish reasons we have a notion of order and an irresistible love of it which influences us in spite of ourselves; that every noble action involves some self-sacrifice and we cannot help respecting anyone who makes sacrifices; that although in making sacrifices we may simply be doing what gives us most pleasure, it is right that we should honour those who give up all that is most precious to them for the pleasure of doing good, increasing their own self-esteem and the opinion others have of them; that those who seek the applause of the public are making a precious compliment to their fellow-men, and saying to them as someone did in antiquity: 'Oh Romans, how many days and nights I have spent in order to win a word of approval from you! One would never take so much trouble for people one despised.'

Madame Le Gendre does not think that Suard talks fluently. I believe she is wrong. As far as I can see, it is his strongest point.

This discussion led me to mention what had just happened at Deuil. The vicar of this parish was transferred to the parish of Grosley. His parishioners loved him so much that in spite of their extreme poverty they would have opened a subscription to ensure that he was no worse off at Grosley than at Deuil, if he had allowed it. A few days ago he went to take over his new parish. In the middle of the *Te Deum Laudamus*, he saw in the congregation a group of his former parishioners in tears; his voice broke and tears came to his eyes. Everyone praised the vicar and his parishioners, and this little incident was an excellent example of the principles which I had been expounding. This conversation was quite to Madame de Blacy's taste and she stayed until half past ten. Then I gave her my arm and went to finish the evening in her house; there we talked of mama and you. 'When are they coming back?' 'Soon.' 'Are you going to Isle?' 'That depends more on the prince than on me.' 'Have you seen him?' 'No.' 'Why not?' 'Because he has gone off to Fontainebleau.' 'When will he be back?' 'I do not know. He has been there for four days and he has still not asked for his horses.' 'So we shall not have mama here for her name-day?' 'I doubt it.' 'I shall write to her.' 'So shall I. Goodnight.'

Mademoiselle Volland, give her my best wishes and a bouquet and a kiss from me along with yours. Say to mama on my behalf all the affectionate things your heart inspires you with and do not be afraid that you will exceed my feelings.

The weather is dismal. The fair lady does you wrong to make you wait all alone in your gloomy mansion, What is she doing in her province? If she was half as bored as the prince is here in Paris, you would have been in Châlons two days ago. Madame Duclos has asked Damilaville whether she should come to Paris. When she is here she only embarrasses him and causes trouble for him at La Briche; he would just as soon she stayed in

Châlons[1] and has told her so. I have not written to her, but my little girl has written for me; it comes to the same thing, and in any case I prefer her reproaches to yours. Once or twice I have picked up my pen to write to her, and then have written to you. But please hurry back here. Do you know that you will very shortly be owing me a bouquet for my name-day.

Given the prince's uncertain situation, I doubt if he will be able to go and meet his fair lady; he is expecting his marching orders with every post. And they are both such touchy, sensitive, temperamental, difficult children that I should not be surprised if they had quarrelled by letter. The people who make the best friends are often the most hopeless lovers. Perhaps the prince, who is an indefatigable moralist, has taken it into his head to give her some advice on their future happiness; even if he has done so in the most tactful, delicate and loving way imaginable, his advice will have been badly received, because despots in general do not care for advice, and all pretty women are despots. Really I cannot stand women who put such value on their favours, except the first time.

Goodbye, my dears; I can hear the heavens dissolving. I do not write to you as often as I should like to, but once I start I cannot stop. I am counting on the effects of solitude and friendship, so that whatever I write, you will never read anything but: he loves us, he loves us, because he thinks we shall have the patience to listen to all his trivial prattle.

By the way, did you know that Madame d'Aine has turned freethinker? A few days ago she announced to us that she thought her soul would rot in the earth together with her body. 'But why do you pray to God then?' 'Upon my word, I have no idea.' 'Don't you believe in mass then?' 'Some days I do, some days I don't.' 'And what happens on the days when you do?' 'I am bad-tempered.' 'And do you go to confession?' 'Why should I?' 'To confess your sins.' 'I don't commit any, and even if I did, what difference would it make if I told a priest about them?' 'Aren't you afraid of hell then?' 'No more than I hope for paradise.' 'But where have you got all these ideas from?' 'From the fine talk of my son-in-law; my word, you would need a good

[1] Monsieur and Madame Duclos now lived at Châlons-sur-Marne, on the way from Paris to Isle. Madame Duclos had been replaced in Damilaville's affections by Madame de Maux.

stock of religion to be left with a single scrap after living in the same house as him. Listen to me, son-in-law, you are the one who has made a mess of my catechism; you will answer for it at the Last Judgement.' 'So you believe in God then?' 'Believe in God! It is so long since I last thought about him, that I couldn't tell you whether I believe in him or not. All I know is that if I am damned I won't be the only one and that going to confession and mass won't make a bit of difference. It's not worth tormenting yourself about nothing. If I had seen this when I was younger, I should perhaps have done a lot of pleasant things which I did not do. But at my age I don't know why I don't believe in anything. I don't gain anything by it. If I don't read the Bible, I'll have to read novels; otherwise I should be bored to tears.' 'But the Bible is an excellent novel.' 'My word, you're right there; I have never read it in that spirit; I'll begin tomorrow; it may make me laugh.' 'Start with Ezekiel.' 'Ah yes, because of that Aholah and that Aholibah and those Assyrians who . . .'[1] 'They don't make men like that today.' 'And what difference does it make to me if they do or they don't? Not one of them would come after me, and if even if a dozen of them did . . .' 'Do you think you would send them next door?' 'That would depend on the moment.' 'You still have moments then?' 'Why not? My word, I believe women keep on having them until their dying day; it's the last sign of life, and once that is dead, you may be sure the rest is dead. You may laugh, all of you, but believe me, any woman who says otherwise is a liar; this is our great secret I am telling you.' 'Don't worry; we shall not take advantage of it.' 'I should think not. But even so, I am not sure; if the only fare available was a woman of my age, I'll be damned if I'd think she was safe, or you either. But let's get back to our unbelief.' 'No, let's forget that; what we are talking about now seems much more amusing to me.' 'My word, you are right.'

And so we spend the evening saying the most ridiculous things. We had put out our candles and lit them again a dozen times. During all this the musician Kohaut had put his hand down the back of her dress and kept on pushing it down and she said as she struggled: 'Look at this disgusting musician who can't keep his hands off musical instruments; stop it now! You will all be

[1] Aholah and Aholibah were great favourites with Voltaire; see *Ezekiel*: 23.

asleep in a quarter of an hour, but I must go and say my prayers.' 'But I thought you said you didn't pray to God.' 'Good heavens, I have to get down on my knees for the sake of my chambermaid.' 'And when you are on your knees, what do you think about?' 'About what we are going to eat tomorrow; this lasts quite a time, and my chambermaid goes off very edified, because she is a devout woman, not that she is any the better for that.'

If I had any room left I would carry on with this chat, though you may have had too much of it already. Goodnight then, my dears.

## 34

*Paris, 10 September 1768*

My dear ladies,

I am doing nothing, absolutely nothing, not even that Salon which I hope Grimm and I will see the end of. Not that I don't go to bed with all sorts of magnificent plans for the next day. But when I get up in the morning I feel a repugnance, a torpor, and an aversion to pen and ink and books, which comes either from laziness or from senility. I prefer to sit with my legs crossed and my arms folded in Madame and Mademoiselle's rooms and waste two or three hours laughing and joking about what they are doing. By the time I have made them really cross, I find it is too late to get down to work; I get dressed and go out. Where do I go? Upon my soul, I can't tell; sometimes to see Naigeon or Damilaville, on other days to see Mademoiselle Bayon, who plays me anything I ask for on her harpsichord. The book-stalls are my last resort. The thing that annoys me about this is that we shall have no grapes or wine. Otherwise the time seems well spent to me.

I had two Englishmen to show around; after seeing everything, they have left and I find I miss them greatly. They weren't at all fanatical about their country and recognised that our language had reached its final perfection, while theirs remained in a state of near-barbarity. 'That is because there is no one who looks after yours', I told them, 'whereas we have forty geese to guard the Capitol.' This comparison seemed all the more apt to them because our geese, like the Roman ones, guard the Capitol without defending it.

The forty geese have just given their prize to a feeble piece of writing by a boy called Sabatin-Langeac. The piece is even more infantile than its author; people attribute it to Marmontel, who read it out at the public session but was unable to conceal its mediocrity even with his winning way of declaiming it. Nevertheless it took the prize away from a certain Monsieur de Rulière who had submitted a satire on the futility of disputes which was excellent both in style and substance, but which was rejected on the pretext that it attacked individuals. The judgement of the geese gave rise to a rather heated exchange between Marmontel and a young poet called Chamfort,[1] a good-looking fellow, quite talented, with all the appearance of modesty and a rich store of self-importance. He is a little balloon that only has to be pricked with a pin to give out a blast of wind. This was how the little balloon began: 'The piece you have chosen must be very good, gentlemen.' 'Why is that?' 'Because it is better than La Harpe's!'[2] 'It could be better than La Harpe's and still be very bad.' 'But I have seen La Harpe's.' 'And did you think it was good?' 'Excellent.' 'That proves that you do not know what you are talking about.' 'If La Harpe's is bad, but still better than young Sabatin's, then Sabatin's must be execrable.' 'Perhaps.' 'But why give the prize to an execrable piece?' 'Why didn't you ask that question when yours won the prize?' etc., etc. All the same, while Marmontel was giving Chamfort a drubbing, the public in its turn was not letting the Academy off lightly.

The man in Geneva is continuing to persecute poor La Bletterie.[3] Here is the latest barb he has shot at him:

> A beggar is complaining loud and high,
> Choiseul gives him some gold out of compassion;
> The fellow then insults the passers-by,
> Choiseul is just and lets the people thrash him.
> Dear La Bletterie, restrain your indignation,
> Receive the alms and blows with resignation.

[1] Nicolas-Sébastien Roch de Chamfort (1741–94) later became famous as a writer of maxims.

[2] Jean-François de la Harpe (1739–1803) is now known principally for his *Cours de littérature*.

[3] Voltaire is 'the man in Geneva'; La Bletterie was a professor at the Collège de France and a member of the Academy of Inscriptions.

Dear La Bletterie wanted the Academy to debate a motion which would have permanently excluded from the Academy any Encyclopedist or anyone connected with the Encyclopedia.

So much for the dishonour of the French Academy; now for the dishonour of the Academy of Painting which I promised to tell you about.

You know that we have here a school of painting, sculpture and architecture and that places in it are open to competition. Students reside in the school for three years; they are given lodging, food, heating, light, and tuition, and an allowance of three hundred francs a year. After their three years here they go to Rome, where we have another school. The students there have the same privileges as those in Paris, and an additional one hundred francs a year. Every year three students go on from the Paris school to the Rome school and are replaced by three new entrants. Imagine the importance of these places to young people who are usually from poor families, who have cost their parents a great deal of money, and who have been working for many years; just think how criminally unfair it is to them when the places are awarded not on the merit of the candidates, but on the personal favour of the judges.

Any student can compete, however strong or weak he may be. The Academy gives a subject. This year it was the triumph of David after his victory over the Philistine Goliath. Every candidate does a sketch and writes his name at the bottom of it. The Academy's first task is to decide which sketches are worthy to compete; the number is usually limited to seven or eight. The young authors of these sketches, painters and sculptors alike, are obliged to follow their qualifying sketches in their paintings or bas-reliefs. They are shut up by themselves and work on their exhibits. When the exhibits are finished, they are put on show to the public for several days, and the Academy awards the prize or the free place on the Saturday following St. Louis's Day.

On that day, the Place du Louvre is full of artists, students, and citizens of all sorts, all waiting in silence for the Academy's decision.

The prize for painting went to a young man called Vincent. This was immediately greeted with acclamations and applause. It was indeed well-deserved. The winner was hoisted on to his comrades' shoulders and carried round the square; after this honourable ovation he was put down at the school. This is a custom which I like and which will please you.

Then everyone waited in silence for the announcement of the sculpture prize. There were three outstanding bas-reliefs. The young students who had done them, and who were hoping that the prize would go to one of them, were saying amicably to one another: 'What I have done is quite good, but yours is beautiful: if you are the winner, I shall not feel too had about it.' Well, ladies, not one of them won it. Intrigue gave it to a certain Moette, Pigalle's pupil. Our friend and his friend Le Moine[1] have covered themselves with shame. The former said to the latter: 'If my pupil does not get the prize, I shall leave the Academy.' And Le Moine was too cowardly to reply: 'If the Academy can only keep you by doing an injustice, it will be more to its credit to lose you.' But let us get back to our crowd on the Place du Louvre.

There was a moment of dumb consternation. A student called Milot, to whom the public, the sensible members of the Academy, and his fellow-students had awarded the prize, was taken ill. Then there was a muttering and then a shouting, with insults, cat-calls, and general fury. It was a terrible uproar. The first academician to come out was the dapper Abbé Laporte, an honorary member. The doorway was blocked; he asked the crowd to let him pass. They made way for him, and as he came past they shouted; 'Pass, you b . . . ass.' Next came the undeserving winner; his youngest comrades grabbed him by the clothes and shouted: 'Scab, rotten scab, we won't let you in, you swine, we'll brain you.' And then there was an even bigger roar, and a chorus of cat-calls so you couldn't hear yourself speak. Poor Moette, shaking in every limb and completely disconcerted, said to them: 'Gentlemen, it wasn't me, it was the Academy', and they replied: 'If you're not as much of a swine as the people who gave you the prize, go back in there and tell them you don't want the place.' While this was going on, a voice was saying: 'Let's put him on all fours and lead him round the square with Milot riding him.' And this is nearly what happened. Meanwhile the academicians were expecting to be hissed and booed and mocked and didn't dare to show their faces. They were not mistaken; they were greeted in the most forceful way imaginable.

[1] The sculptor Jean-Baptiste Le Moine had been Falconet's teacher.

Cochin[1] shouted out to them: 'Those who are discontented give me their names', but they didn't listen to him; they hissed and booed and mocked. Pigalle, with his hat on his head and that boorish tone of voice you know, turned to a bystander whom he took for an artist but who wasn't one, and asked if him if he was a better judge than he, Pigalle. The bystander in question pushed down his hat over his eyes and replied that he didn't know much about bas-reliefs, but he knew an insolent fellow when he saw one, and Pigalle was one. Perhaps you think that then night came and everything calmed down. Not quite.

The indignant students ganged together and planned a second attack for the next meeting of the Academy. They found out exactly who had been for Milot and who had been for Moette. The following Saturday everyone gathered at the Place du Louvre with all the instruments necessary to create an uproar and the firm intention of using them; but this intention gave way before the fear of the police and prison. They contented themselves with forming two lines between which all their masters would be forced to pass. Boucher, Dumont, Vanloo,[2] and various other defenders of true merit came out first, and were duly surrounded, welcomed, embraced, and applauded. Then came Pigalle. Hardly had he set foot between the lines than there was a shout: 'About turn', and everyone turned round and gave him a posterior salute. Cochin received the same honours, as did Monsieur and Madame Vien and the rest of them.

The academicians have had all the bas-reliefs broken, so as to destroy every trace of their injustice. You may like to know what Milot's was like; since I saw it, here is a description for you.

On the right are three great Philistines, all downcast and shamefaced; one of them has his hands bound behind his back and the other two are having theirs bound by a young Israelite. Then comes the young David, being carried by women to his chariot; one of the women has thrown herself on the ground and is kissing his legs, others are lifting him up and yet another one is crowning him. Next you see his chariot pulled by two fiery

[1] Charles-Nicolas Cochin was an engraver and draughtsman and secretary of the Academy of Painting. The frontispiece to the *Encyclopédie* is his work.

[2] Louis-Michel Vanloo (1707–71) was nephew to Carle, whose death was reported to Sophie in 1765, and author of a famous portrait of Diderot.

steeds; a charioteer is standing by one of the horses, holding them by the bridle, and on the point of handing their reins to the conqueror. In the foreground a sturdy Israelite is thrusting a spear into Goliath's head, which is lying there upside down, all enormous and horrible, with the hair falling around it in all directions. Further off, on the left, there are women dancing, singing, and tuning their instruments. Among the dancers a sort of bacchante is banging a drum and leaping about extraordinarily gracefully with her arms and legs in the air. In the foreground another dancer is holding her child by the hand; the child is dancing too, but his eyes are fixed on the horrible head, and he has an expression of mixed joy and terror. In the background are men and women with their mouths open and their arms raised in acclamation of the victor.

It was claimed that this was not the subject that was set, but the reply was that they were criticizing the candidate for showing genius. They objected to the chariot, which is not even off the subject. Cochin was cleverer; he wrote to me that everyone judges according to his own impressions, and that the prize-winner had seemed to him to possess more talent. Those are the words of a man devoid of taste or honesty. The others admitted that Milot's bas-relief was indeed excellent, but claimed that Moette was more talented; they were asked what use prizes were if you judged the person and not the work.

But here is a curious coincidence for you: at the very same moment that Milot was being deprived of his due by the Academy, I was reading a letter from Falconet which said: 'I saw a student of Le Moine's called Milot, who seemed to be a decent and talented fellow. See if you can get him to join me here; I leave the conditions to you.' I rushed round to Le Moine's house and told him what Falconet proposed. Le Moine raised his hands to heaven and exclaimed: 'Providence! providence!' and I retorted gruffly: 'Providence! providence! Do you think providence is there to put your mistakes right?' Milot came in and I invited him to come and see me. The next day he was at my house; the young man was as drawn and dishevelled as if he had been ill for a long time; his eyes were red and swollen and he said to me in a heart-rending voice: 'After being a burden to my poor parents for seventeen years, just when I was beginning to hope! After working for seventeen years from morning till night! Oh, I am finished, sir! It would not be so bad if I could hope to win next year's prize, but nothing could be less certain with competitors like Stouffe and Foucaut!' Those are the names of his two rivals this year. I proposed to him that he should go to Russia; he asked me for the rest of the day to think it over and discuss it with his friends. He came back to see me a few days ago and gave me this answer: 'I am extremely grateful for your offer, sir; I quite understand how advantageous it would be to me, but our calling is not one to be followed for gain. I must give the academicians a chance to make up for their injustice; I must go to Rome or perish!'

So you see, my good friends, how it is possible to discourage and distress the deserving, to dishonour yourself and the body to which you belong, to bring unhappiness to one student and the same to another who will be reproached with his success by his fellow-students for years to come, and perhaps even to be the cause of bloodshed.

The Academy was planning to decimate the students. Boucher, the dean of the Academy, refused to attend this debate. Vanloo argued that they were all equally guilty or innocent, that they were not governed by a military code, and that he did not answer for the consequences. And indeed, if this plan had been accepted, the victimized students were resolved to stick Cochin full of holes. Cochin, who is envied because of his success, has had to bear the brunt of the students' hostility and the criticism of the public.

A few days ago I wrote to him: 'There! you have been jeered at, reviled and ridiculed by your pupils. They could easily be in the wrong, but it is a hundred to one they are not. They have eyes, those boys, and it would be the first time they had made a mistake.'

And indeed, hardly are the exhibits on show than they are judged by the students, who declare: 'That is the winner.'

In connection with all this I heard about a singular action of Falconet's. His son was once competing for the prize. The paintings and sculptures were being exhibited, and young Falconet's picture was no good. His father took him by the arm, led him to the gallery, and said: 'Look at them and judge for yourself.' The boy looked to the ground and said nothing. Then his father turned to his colleagues the academicians and said to them: 'His painting is feeble, but he hasn't the courage to withdraw it. Well, if he will not, gentlemen, I will.' Whereupon he put his son's picture under his arm and walked out. Oh! if only this rough diamond, who is fair-minded and detests Pigalle, had been in Paris for this session of the Academy! . . .

Since the poems which competed for the Academy prize have been published, someone has composed this couplet about the production of young Sabatin—Saint-Florentin-Phélypeaux—Langeac:

These verses are sublime, let all men know,
By order of Louis—and Phélypeaux.[1]

There! mademoiselle, that is my fourth page, and if one line of mine is worth a page of yours, where does that leave you now? When will you ever pay your debts? But don't lose any sleep over it; I am a man of conscience and I know that an ounce of gold is worth a ton of base metal.

It is four days since Damilaville moved to the Rue Saint-Honoré and three days since Madame Duclos left Paris. She does not expect to see her friend again, and the separation has left her broken-hearted. She is a noble, kind soul. She has suffered cruelly. Whenever Madame de M . . .[2] was there, the patient treated Madame Duclos exactly like a nurse. When she was not, he treated her civilly again.

I went to see him the day before yesterday. The lady in question was there, together with her friend, the charming dean, Grimm, d'Alembert, Madame d'Épinay, various other people, and me. Each of these birds had its own special song, and I can assure you that you would have enjoyed listening to them all. Someone observed that coquetry was natural and common to all animals, and that man should have his own way of being coquettish; this was enough to set us off on the different customs of the nations of the world. We had the savage roasting himself with matches, the Muslim hacking at himself with his knife, the Spaniard catching his death of cold under a gutter playing his guitar, the Frenchman pirouetting, whistling, bantering and

[1] Louis XV's minister Phélypeaux de Saint-Florentin was said by a malicious contemporary to take a paternal interest in the children of Madame de Langeac, one of whom was this young Sabatin.

[2] Madame de Maux, who was looking after Damilaville during the illness of which he was to die before the year was out.

showing off his legs and teeth. The dean is all for pure physical love with none of the feeble morality of passion. With women it is a tactical matter; this is proved by the broadshouldered yokels who treat them like dirt and have them clinging round them. My opinion was that women only stayed with these people because they were never sure of being loved. It's a question of vanity. This text can lead a long way. I left them to it.

On my way home the wind, which had been blowing fit to take the horns off a goat, had died down; the air was balmy and the sky was full of stars and I felt happy thinking of the lovely walks it promised my good friends.

I haven't even mentioned the patient's health. He is weaker and thinner than ever; he has a continuous fever with unremitting pain and glands more swollen than before—there are even some new ones under his chin. The axillaries are so big that he cannot lower his arms. So much the worse, says Bordeu; so much the better, says Tronchin. I am very much afraid that Bordeu is an excellent doctor. Madame Duclos told me that the symptoms and pains were all exactly as he had predicted. Otherwise, the apartment is as pleasant as can be, with the shrubberies of President Hénault and others under the windows and the mass of trees in the Tuileries a bit further off.

Well then! the sublime letter to the good Saint-Florentin did not go in vain. He sent an officer with a few twenty-franc pieces which were left discreetly on the mantelpiece of the person in question, and he has promised to help and to make a visit in person. So knowing how to write is not totally useless; eloquence can move stones. Now can you doubt the stories of Amphion and Orpheus, my ancestors?

I am drinking milk in the mornings and lemonade at night; I am doing well on it and this surprises me. The Baron proves on the authority of Stahl and Becher that I am wrong . . . to be surprised.

I should like to be able to send you another fine letter to look at, together with a request from Poinsinet and a reply to your last, but I have no margin left. Remind me about all these things and about a fable and one or even two stories of mine.

Keep well, all three of you; that is one of the articles of our treaty. I have this moment had a card from one of the Artaud ladies, who asks me to tell you of the death of Monsieur Dupérier on the eve of the Assumption. He died at two in the afternoon and by three the seals were affixed.

My regards to you all. There is no room for more.

## 35

*Paris, 8 October 1768*

Here is another thing. Laverdy[1] worked with the King on Sunday and went off full of confidence to his country house at Neuville to see to the arrangements they had agreed upon. He was expecting several people whom he had asked to come and see him on Monday. On Tuesday he intended to return to his normal routine. But on that day Monsieur de Saint-Florentin appeared at ten in the morning. When he saw him Laverdy said: 'Sir, it is too early in the morning to be visiting', and he was right.

They say that the King never appears so relaxed and friendly to a minister as on the eve of his fall from favour. I am not sure if this is so, but do you know that I would not blame him? Courtiers are so used to the different expressions of their master that if he did not put on a calm face they would immediately see what he was up to and he would be so pestered with petitions that he would be unable to dismiss a servant with whom he was dissatisfied without upsetting many others whom perhaps he loved. This kind of dissimulation is all the more necessary for a ruler who is easily swayed; not to speak of the insistent demands of potential successors and their protectors. It is almost the only way of retaining his freedom of choice and preventing all the slanders which make his decision more difficult.

We have just witnessed an incident here which proves that all our fine sermons on tolerance have not borne much fruit yet. A young man of good family, an apothecary's apprentice according to some and a grocer's according to others, wanted to follow a chemistry course. His master consented on condition that he pay for his keep; the apprentice agreed to this. At the end of the quarter the master asked for money and the apprentice paid him.

[1] Laverdy had just been dismissed from his post as Controller General of Finances.

Shortly afterwards came another demand to which the apprentice replied that he did not even owe money for a quarter. The master denied that he had paid the previous instalment. The case came before the courts. The master was put on oath. He swore he had had no money. Hardly had he perjured himself when the apprentice produced his receipt, and the master was fined and dishonoured. He was a scoundrel and deserved it, but the apprentice was a scatterbrain to say the least and it has cost him more than his life is worth. He had received two copies of *Christianity Unveiled*[1] on payment or otherwise from a pedlar called Lescuyer and had sold one of these to his master. The master denounced him to the lieutenant of police. The pedlar, the pedlar's wife, and the apprentice were all arrested and they have just been pilloried, whipped, and branded, the apprentice condemned to nine years in the galleys, the pedlar to five, and the wife to life imprisonment. The sentence mentions not only *Christianity Unveiled*, but also *The Man with Forty Crowns*[2] and *The Vestal*,[3] a tragedy which we read in manuscript.

There has been an outcry against Sartine. But do you see what this sentence will lead to? A pedlar brings me a prohibited book. If I buy more than one copy I am supposedly guilty of unlawful trading and liable to the most ferocious punishment. You know *The Man with Forty Crowns* and you will be hard put to it to guess why it has been stigmatized along with the other books. It is because of the resentment aroused in our rulers by a certain article entitled 'Tyrant' in the *Philosophical Dictionary*; perhaps you will remember it. They will never forgive Voltaire for saying that it is better to be faced by a single fierce monster that you can avoid than by a whole troop of lesser beasts yapping at your heels. And that is why the *Philosophical Dictionary* was burned in the case of young La Barre even though he did not possess the book.[4]

I fear that for all his reputation, his protectors, his rare

[1] *Le Christianisme dévoilé*, by Baron d'Holbach. Subversive books such as this did not receive the official *privilège* or the semi-official *permission tacite* and were therefore published clandestinely. Penalties for infringement of the publishing laws were imposed inconsistently, but could be very harsh.

[2] *L'Homme aux quarante écus*, a philosophical tale by Voltaire.

[3] *Éricie ou la vestale*, a play in three acts by Dubois-Fontenelle.

[4] The young Chevalier de la Barre was tortured and executed in 1766 for failing to respect a religious procession; Voltaire took up his case.

talents, and his admirable books these people will do our poor patriarch a bad turn one of these days. Of course posterity will pour the ignominy with which they thought to cover him back on to their own heads, but what good will that do him when he is reduced to ashes? Did you know that three days ago they were deliberating putting out a warrant for his arrest?

To return to the two poor wretches who have been condemned to the galleys: when they have served their time, what will become of them? There will be nothing left to them but to become highwaymen. Dishonourable penalties, which take away every honest means of subsistence from a man, are worse than the death penalty which takes away his life.

I have seen Monsieur de la Fargue looking very thin and haggard and sickly. He began by giving me news of you, your health, your desire to see me at Isle, where I should like to be; then he went on to the strange effect of my letter to Monsieur Trouard. It would be just my luck if out of a dozen affairs of this kind[1] which I have been involved in over the last three or four months, this one, which interests me far more than any of the others, was the only one in which I failed.

I am due to dine one of these days with Monsieur Dubucq and a great lady whose name is being kept a secret from me. As you can imagine, Madame de Blacy, I shall not forget our little cousin, who is no longer living off monkeys and parrots by now, I trust.

There's something else I forgot to mention. If the office in the Rue Sainte-Anne is closed, as they say it will be, what will become of our love?

They also say that the interest rate is going back to five per cent.

Just you dare complain to me, mademoiselle! Count my letters and make your apologies, if you please.

Damilaville? Alas! poor Damilaville is suffering; every day he is more thin and bent and shrivelled; he cannot even walk now. If Tronchin can save him, I will believe in medicine and its miracles.

It is no longer the child who is ill, but the mother; her gout has gone up to her head, her chest, and her eyes. It will all come to nothing; she will get off with a fright and we shall get off with

[1] Requests for favours on behalf of his friends.

a few squalls of bad temper from her. Madame Diderot is one of the few women who cannot endure pain.

For the last week I have been plagued by stomach pains, but they will come to nothing too, as I shall do nothing about them.

But don't you go catching cold, by God; light a fire if you feel chilly. I am not talking to you or Madame de Blacy, who are a pair of limp chickens; you can be ill as much as you like. I mean mama, who has only to wish it to keep well. Really, it is maddening.

*Did I know what day it was on the fourth of October?*[1] I do not even deign to answer that question.

I should love all those bouquets, for I like kissing and I like being kissed even more. But save it all up until your return. It won't go bad with keeping. One of the things which made me happiest was to learn from Monsieur de la Fargue that I would see you again in six weeks. Six weeks seemed to me a shorter time than a month and a half.

Don't go and give Monsieur Le Gendre the credit for all that fine eloquence which dazzles you; it is just bits and pieces he remembered from the various letters of condolence he received.[2] Friend Digeon has other things to do than arouse the sluggish emotions of his future father-in-law. However, the latter does very well to try and cajole you both. He does not know the secret.

No wine! So you may say, mademoiselle! My sister is very pleased with her grape harvest. My only fear is that the wine will not keep. The cure for that is to drink it more quickly.

My compliments on your harvest. If the high price of corn continues, that is because there is none of last year's crop left, and this year's has not been threshed yet. I am not persuaded about the monopoly. A monopoly on corn cannot do any harm unless it is enforced by law.

And what are you doing about Monsieur Gras?[3] Let him buy and sell grain as much as he likes, so long as he doesn't set you all on fire. All you need to do is to ask mama to lay down the law and use her big voice.

[1] Madame Volland's name-day.
[2] On the death of his wife Marie-Charlotte; this is Diderot's only reference to her death.
[3] The manager of the Volland estate at Isle.

Heaven be praised! Dom Micou Marin[1] has gone at last, and will no longer be able to tire you to death. It's a mystery to me if he hasn't sent on at least two letters to you, as it feels as if I have been writing nearly every day.

Prince Golitsyn is in Brussels; he will be spending two months there. Then he will go on to Berlin and spend the winter there if he is left in peace. From Berlin he will go back to Saint Petersburg and I insist that he should take his wife with him, for they say that if there is anything she lacks it is not guile.[2] So much could be said in praise of almost every woman, excepting always the sheep of God, whom I love for her rarity and for many other excellent qualities. Ah! if only she were willing for one year . . . Mademoiselle Volland, put it to her again.

So, you are following in the tracks of your caretaker and you need a cleric too! Well, it is not too bad as a makeshift. A priest without his cassock is a man like the rest of them. Ask Abbé Marin or Madame de Maux in Vitry.

No, mademoiselle, I shall not say I love you any more, or if I do, it will be in spite of myself, out of sheer habit.

I think I said I hated you the day before yesterday. Don't believe it. It is not true.

Give my love to mama and Madame de Blacy, and let's have no more of these colds; they may be harmless, but they annoy me.

## 36

*Paris, 22 November 1768*

My dear ladies,

You have still not decided on your departure date! Surely all this bad weather will hasten your return. What can you do at Isle that you could not do still better in the Rue Saint-Thomas-du-Louvre?[3] There is a little garden there to catch the fleeting glimpses of the sun, friends whom you want to see and who are waiting for your arrival, a little green table to rest your elbows on, first-hand news both true and false, a fireplace to huddle round in the freezing weather, and sundry amusements which

[1] Apparently Diderot's nickname for Abbé Marin, a frequent visitor to Isle.
[2] Golitsyn married a young German countess in the autumn of 1768.
[3] At Madame de Blacy's house.

you cannot find in the country when rain, winds and frost confine you to the house. There are days when three or four of us would make shift to replace Abbé Marin.

Where is the time when you would have been overjoyed by my impatience and ill-humour and anger, and delighted that I did not give my letters or your replies time to arrive, when you would have complained at two days without word from me as if it had been two weeks? That would seem unjust to you now. Your calculations are flawless, you could not be more reasonable than you have become, you are never cross now, and you do not want me to be cross. So be it: I shall not be cross.

Madame Vanloo nearly died of a dartrous humour on her chest, but she has stopped spitting purulent blood and for the time being she seems as good as new.

Madame de Coaslin[1] will not be seeing me. I told Monsieur Dubucq as much quite firmly when he came to see me, just as I was opening Madame de Blacy's great parcel. Tell that excellent mother that she can set her mind at rest about her son. He has everything he needs. I have Monsieur Dubucq's word of honour for it, and he is not a man to promise what he has no intention of doing or to assure you that something has been done when it has not. The letters you send me by way of Damilaville come post-free; I did not reply about this sooner because it is of absolutely no importance.

*How do I know Mademoiselle Guimare?*[2]—Why, there have always been scores of ways of getting to know her, and at my age there are scores of reasons for doing so. You find all sorts of things in these ladies of easy virtue that you would not hope to find in a respectable woman, quite apart from the great advantage of being yourself with them, not vain about your good qualities or ashamed of your bad ones.

In any case I have to thank Monsieur de Falbaire, the author of *The Honest Criminal*, who for some reason sees a lot of her, for saving me from the ambush of Monsieur Dubucq and Madame de Coaslin by his indiscretion.

I went to the mysterious tryst; but I refused point-blank to do what was asked of me. *And what was that?*—If mama starts to ponder it, she will find the answer before she has done two

[1] The 'great lady' referred to on p. 182.

[2] A dancer at the Opera, notorious for the scandals of her private life.

seams. As for you, ladies, I advise you not to tax your brains. It is too hard for the likes of you.

Why the devil doesn't your nun throw away her habit and go and hide in some out-of-the-way spot where she can live and die in peace? Give her my advice, which I am sure Madame de Blacy will not disapprove of. It would take Epictetus in person not to be damned in a cell.

I'll do my best to have those fables of Voltaire sent to you; but it would be nice of you to come for them yourselves. I ought not to send you distractions. If you can have the town in the country, I see no reason for coming back from the country to the town.

*Have I made it up with Grimm?*—Oh yes, more or less, I think. It was just as I predicted; I had all the unhappiness and still didn't get out of the visit. The prince[1] came and spent a couple of hours with me incognito. This was on Wednesday. On Thursday I spent the whole day with him at the Baron's without knowing who he was, or so they all thought. But the Baron had warned me and they were hoist with their own petard. I played my part beautifully.

Apropos of Sainte-Périne, the bride was a niece of Monsieur de Neufond. I have only discovered this today; you can imagine how important it is that this whole affair should be forgotten.

I proved to our artist,[2] two hours before she left, that in less than fifteen months she had spent approximately sixteen thousand francs. She has gone now. She is in Brussels. The prince will take her back with honour to her family and her native land, and it will not be my fault if her son is not an ambassador's secretary.

Friend Naigeon is thoroughly entangled. *Eheu! quanto laboras in Caribdi, digne puer meliore flamma!* Get the Abbé Marin to explain this Latin to you.

What is more, the fair lady nearly died of a hysteric vapour and a sudden inflammation of the lower abdomen with a loss of blood.

You are right to feel rather sorry that you cannot read the Salon; there are honestly some rather fine things in it and others which are less serious and more entertaining.

[1] The Prince of Saxe-Gotha.

[2] Madame Therbouche, a mediocre German painter, whom Diderot looked after during her unsuccessful stay in Paris.

I do not know who will be defending the misbaptized young lady. But if you have reflected a little on this case, you will have seen that it is more difficult than it appears at first sight.

Before being so definite about your punctuality, I should like to know what number I have reached.

There is no good wine left in my sister's cellar. She has sent me the only two wretched barrels that remained.

Don't expect me to believe what you say about mama. Here is the truth of the matter. You persuade her that she has bad legs. Madame de Blacy keeps her company and off you go through the fields, all by youself with the Abbé. Very clever!

I am quite enchanted by my daughter. She says that her mama prays to God and her papa does good; that my way of thinking is like a pair of slippers, which you don't put on for everyone to look at, but to keep your feet warm; that there are actions which help us and harm others, like garlic which you don't eat even if you like it because it smells unpleasant; that when she sees all that goes on around her, she hasn't the courage to laugh at the Egyptians; that if she had a large family with one child who was really, really bad, she could never bring herself to pick him up by the feet and throw him head first into the stove. And all this in an hour and a half's talk while we were waiting for dinner.

She seemed so advanced to me that last Sunday, when her mother sent me out for a walk with her, I decided to tell her all that it means to be a woman, beginning with this question: 'Do you know what the difference is between the sexes?' This led me to talk about all the pretty speeches which women have to listen to. 'They mean', I said, ' "Mademoiselle, would you be so good as to dishonour yourself, lose your position in society, shut yourself up in a convent for life, and be the death of your father and mother, just to please me?" ' I taught her what to say and what not to say, what to hear and what not to hear; the right her mother had to be obeyed by her; how monstrously ungrateful a child would be who brought unhappiness to the woman who had risked her life to bring her into the world; that she owed me her love and respect as she might to a benefactor, but that with her mother it was different; what was the true foundation of decency, the need to conceal those parts of the body the sight of which would be an invitation to vice. I told her everything I could decently say, and she remarked that if she did wrong now, she would be much more to blame, because she would no longer have the excuse of ignorance or curiosity. Talking of the way milk is formed in the breasts and the necessity of either using it to feed the child or getting rid of it in another way, she exclaimed: 'Oh! papa, how horrible to throw your child's food down the privy!' Just think what I could do with a mind like that, if I dared! All I would have to do would be to leave a few books lying about.

I have asked a few sensible people what they thought of this talk and they all approved of it. Could it be that it is no use condemning something when there is no cure for it?

She told me that she had never given any thought to these matters, because she supposed the time would come for her to learn about them, that she had not thought about marriage yet, but that if she was troubled by the desire, she would be quite open about it and say frankly to her mother and me: 'Papa, mama, I want to be married', since she could see nothing shameful about it.

If I were to lose this child, I think I should die of grief. I love her more than I can say.

A religion which lays down painful practices for the devout usually makes them bad-tempered with those around them.

Abbé Galiani has at last come out into the open. If there is one thing that is certain in political economy, it is that it is madness to export grain. I swear to you, my dear, that no one before now had even begun to answer this question; I went down on my knees and begged him to publish his ideas.

Here is just one of his principles: What does it mean to sell corn?—It means exchanging corn for money.—Not a bit of it: it means exchanging corn for corn. And how can it ever be profitable to exchange the corn you have for the corn which is sold to you?

He showed us all the ramifications of this law—and they are immense. He explained to us the cause of the present high prices, and we saw that no one had even guessed at it. Never in my life have I listened to him with so much pleasure.

Once again, my good friends, be careful that the wicked woman does not see through you. But what sort of hitch can get in the way of your reimbursement?

I don't know what you mean with your Charenton gate; either you have misread me, or I did not know what I was writing.

I told you what happened to Madame Bouchard's portrait; in spite of all the artist's efforts it remained rather cloudy and this could only have been put right by painting it all over again.

Yes indeed, the young king[1] would have seen all of us. This was arranged in spite of the efforts of his ministers and ours. We were due to be dining with the Baron von Gleichen and he was to have arrived unexpectedly, but he has succumbed to all the boredom and the ceremonies and fallen ill. The Baron affirms that it is only a pleasure deferred. I hope so, if only to show the asses that we are appreciated elsewhere.

I did not want to attend this dinner; this was what brought about exactly the same scene between the Baron and me as I had had a week earlier with Grimm.

We have no luck with our charity. We gave hospitality to a compatriot who had to come to Paris on some unpleasant business. For three months she shared my daughter's bed and amused herself by sowing dissension among my people with her chatter.

While you are leading your stay-at-home lives at Isle, you do not realize how useful you could be to me in Paris. I have just received an order from the Empress to purchase the Gaignat collection.

It is raining cannon-balls in the house of the Lord; I am in fear and trembling lest one of the intrepid gunners should be hurt by the recoil. We have had the *Philosophical Letters*, translated or supposedly translated from the English of Toland, the *Letter to Eugénie*, *The Sacred Contagion*, *The Life of David or the Man after God's Own Heart*; it is like a thousand devils running riot. Ah! Madame de Blacy, I very much fear the Son of God is at the door, the coming of Elijah is nigh, and the reign of Antichrist is upon us. Every day when I get up in the morning I look out of my window to see whether the great whore of Babylon is not already walking the streets with her cup in her hand and whether there are not any of the signs foretold in the firmament. What are you doing at Isle? Hurry back here, so that we can be present together at the general resurrection of the dead. If you wait for the sun to be extinguished, how will you get back to Paris?

[1] Christian VII, King of Denmark, who was visiting Paris at this time.

It's impossible to travel when you can't see the back of your hand.

No sign of Monsieur Trouard. Perhaps it wouldn't be a bad idea if I went to see him.

I send you all my greetings and embrace you all together and then separately, making the appropriate distinctions.

I am keeping well here too, with lemonade in the morning and cold milk at night. Gatti claims that this diet is not as mad as you might think.

I cannot go off to sleep as easily as you, mademoiselle, though it is high time I did.

## 37

*Paris, 23 August 1769*

Excellent, my love; you tell me how you have been spending your time, and amusing yourself, and how your harvest is progressing. You assume that all this interests me, and indeed it does. Your barns and granaries are really full then, are they? You will be rich then, and no one will go hungry this year except the lazy. You cannot imagine how glad this makes me.

That foot of mama's worries me. I don't know why it is but I am more concerned for her health than for yours. Yet I love you all equally. Well, not quite; mama and her eldest daughter would not like that. You can read them that if you wish; I hope they will have the good sense to understand me and not take offence. There is a loving word for you, and from me too; who knows, it may bring more in its train.

My rough drafts are indecipherable.[1] The man who makes copies of them for Grimm will have me to thank for the loss of his eyesight; I, meanwhile, will still see as well as ever. Believe me, I am as anxious to send you any worthwhile things I have written as you are to receive them. Don't you see that next to the pleasure of helping my friend, my greatest reward is to give my ladies a moment's pleasure?

On Thursday I am going to Le Grandval for the day. We

[1] Grimm was away on a prolonged visit to Germany; in his absence Diderot was keeping the 'shop' of the *Correspondance littéraire* supplied with material.

have been quite unable to get a coach-party together. This year seems to be a bad one for friendship. I hope the epidemic will spare ours.

Well, *The Father*[1] has been played at last. Molé is sublime as Saint-Albin, Brizard is not bad, Mademoiselle Préville is quite good as Cécile, the Germeuil is bad, and Auger is mediocre as the Commander except in a few scenes. Mademoiselle Doligny's Sophie is negligible. But to do them all justice, they have put all their skill into the production and they play so well together that the harmony of the whole makes up for deficiencies of detail. And then, even though I am the author, I must say that there is such rapidity and violence and strength in the work that it is impossible to kill it. In any case, it got across to the audience and won their applause. I don't know how to describe this applause. At every performance there has been a fearful crowd and an uproar. No one can remember a play having such a success, especially at a first performance and the play to all intents and purposes a new one. Everyone is agreed that it is a great and beautiful work, and I cannot help thinking so too. Indeed it was quite a surprise to me. It is far more effective in the theatre than on the page. Your absence robbed us all of a great pleasure. If all the parts were as well played as Saint-Albin, it would be irresistible. It would be no good setting me a task like that today, I could never do it. I no longer have the head that is needed to put together a machine of that kind. Duclos[2] said as he came out of the theatre that three plays like that a year would be the end of tragedy. Let them once get used to that kind of emotion, and then see if they can bear to sit through Destouches and La Chaussée.[3] I wanted to know if my way or Sedaine's was the right way of writing comedy. Now there can be no doubt about it, either for me or for anyone else.

My friends are beside themselves with joy; I have seen them all. Can you believe that Marmontel was in tears when he embraced me!

My daughter has been; she came home dumbfounded with astonishment and enthusiasm. In the middle of all this, you will

[1] Diderot's comedy *Le Père de famille* first published in 1758.
[2] Not the Duclos of Châlons, but Charles-Pinot Duclos (1704–72), novelist, author of the *Considérations sur les mœurs de ce siècle*, and Secretary of the French Academy.
[3] Authors of comedies and sentimental plays in the first half of the century.

imagine me full of happiness, yet I am not; I don't know what is going on in the bottom of my soul to upset me, but I am depressed.

Poor Grimm will be back the very last day before the play comes off.

I am worn out with his *Correspondance*. If you could only see what a volume of work it is, and how many books it means reading, you would think I had been reading and writing from morning to night.

Well then, the Company of the Indies has been abolished and Abbé Morellet has virtually dishonoured himself. He has written a pamphlet against the Company and shown himself to be a despicable mercenary who sells his pen to the government against his fellow-citizens. Monsieur Necker[1] has replied to him in such serious, lofty and scornful terms that he must feel crushed. The Abbé intends to reply; in other words after stabbing a man in the back he wants the further pleasure of trampling on his corpse. He is more far-sighted than all the rest of us; a year from now everyone will have forgotten about the despicable deed and he will be receiving the pension he has been promised.

Goodbye, my dear and loving friend. Turn your cheeks to me so that I may kiss them and wish you a happy name-day. Monsieur Perronet, who was sitting by me just now at the theatre, has charged me to add another flower to my bouquet.

Mama and Madame de Blacy, will you both be so kind as to give Mademoiselle Volland a kiss for me.

My regards to you all.

I have seen Madame Bouchard a second time; her husband looked better to me.

## 38

*Paris, 31 August 1769*

My dear ladies,

I am absolutely worn out. It's high time Grimm came home and took back the key of his shop. I am tired of this job, and you

[1] Jacques Necker (1732–1804) was a financier and twice a minister before the Revolution. His wife's *salon* was much frequented by the *philosophes*.

must admit it's the most tedious job in the world reading all the tedious books which come out. Even if he offered me my weight in gold (and I am no featherweight), I should refuse to do any more. Rejoice; at last I am completely rid of that new edition of the *Encyclopedia*, thanks to the impertinence of one of its promoters. That little fellow Panckoucke,[1] puffed up with the arrogance of a parvenu, thought he could treat me as he apparently treats a few poor devils who depend on him for their daily bread —and they pay through the nose for it if they have to swallow all his stupid remarks; well, he took it into his head to carry on the same way here, but it did him no good. I let him have his head for a while, then I got up suddenly, took him by the arm and said: 'Monsieur Panckoucke, wherever you are, in the street, in church or in a house of ill fame, whoever you are talking to, you should always keep a civil tongue in your head. But you ought to be particularly careful when you are speaking to someone as touchy as I am, and in his own house. You can go to hell, you and your book. I haven't the slightest intention of working on it. You could give me twenty thousand louis and I should still want nothing to do with it, not even if I could do the work in seconds. Kindly get out of here and leave me in peace.' That way I think I am free of one worry.

The *Father* has continued to have a huge success. It has been playing to full houses, even though Paris is deserted. The day after tomorrow is the last performance; they don't want to play it too often. They are saving it up for next winter; and in any case Molé wouldn't be able to keep it up any longer.

A week ago I was sitting in the stalls between Monsieur Perronet and Madame de La Ruette. I invited myself to go and see the work on his bridge at Neuilly, on condition that there would only be four of us, himself included. All well and good. The day came. We had arranged to meet at my house. It wasn't Monsieur Perronet who came for me, but Monsieur de Senneville. We set off and when we got there, there were fourteen or fifteen of us at table, not counting the master of the house, who didn't turn up. Everything went off very well. Monsieur de Senneville was extremely gay and affable. We spoke briefly of Madame Le Gendre. He admitted that he had been a little

[1] Charles-Joseph Panckoucke (1736–98) is best known for his publication of the *Encyclopédie méthodique*, a rearranged version of Diderot's *Encyclopédie*.

heartsore for her. We came back together in Monsieur Perronet's carriage. He put me down at the swing-bridge and we parted quite good friends.

I am living in my dressing-gown a lot of the time, reading and writing; writing quite good things about the very bad things I read. I see no one, because there's no one left in Paris. Monsieur Bouchard came to see me, and I was very glad to see him. To come all the way from the Rue des Vieux-Augustins to the Rue Taranne and climb up to the fourth floor is a sign that he is in good health.

When there are no new books to review, I make summaries of books which do not exist yet, but ought to.

When this resource, which is quite fruitful, lets me down, I have another one, which is to write short works of my own.

I have written a dialogue between d'Alembert and me. We talk quite gaily, and quite clearly too, in spite of the dryness and obscurity of the subject. This dialogue is followed by a second one, which is much longer and serves to explain the first one more fully. It is called *D'Alembert's Dream*. The characters are: d'Alembert dreaming, his friend Mademoiselle d'Espinasse,[1] and Bordeu the doctor. If I had wanted to sacrifice some of the richness of the subject matter in return for a nobler tone, I should have chosen Democritus, Hippocrates, and Leucippe; but that way verisimilitude would have confined me to the narrow limits of ancient philosophy, and that would have been too great a price to pay. It is the height of extravagance, but at the same time it is the most profound philosophy. It is quite cunning to have put my ideas into the mouth of a dreamer. You often have to dress up wisdom as folly to gain admittance for it. I had rather they said: 'But that isn't as mad as you might think', than: 'Listen, here are some great truths.'

Meanwhile my little girl and I are still going for our walks. Last time I set out to make her understand that there is no virtue which is not doubly rewarded, by the pleasure of acting well and that of gaining the goodwill of others, and no vice which is not doubly punished, by our secret remorse and by the repugnance which we are bound to arouse in others. It was a fruitful text. We ran over most of the virtues; then I painted for her the

[2] Diderot's mistake for Julie de Lespinasse (1732–76), author of a famous series of love-letters.

envious man with his hollow eyes and his pale thin face, the glutton with his ruined stomach and his gouty legs, the lecher with his asthmatic chest and the remains of various illnesses which are never really cured, or only cured to the detriment of the rest of the body. It is going very well; we shall finish up with very few prejudices, but plenty of discretion, good morals, and rules of conduct which are sound and common to all times and all peoples. She was the author of this last reflection.

Yesterday, I was at a very strange dinner. I spent almost the whole day at the house of a mutual friend with two monks who were anything but bigoted. One of them read us the first part of an atheist treatise,[1] very freshly and vigorously written and full of bold new ideas; I was edified to learn that his doctrine was the prevailing orthodoxy in their corridors. What's more, these two monks were among the powers-that-be in their house. They were witty, gay, decent, knowledgeable men. Whatever you believe, you always have morals when you spend three quarters of your time studying; I would bet that these atheist monks are the most virtuous in their monastery. The thing which amused me was the efforts of our apostle of materialism to find a sanction for laws in the eternal order of things. But what will amuse you far more is the candour with which the apostle affirmed that his system, which attacked all that is most sacred, was quite innocent and did not lay him open to any disagreeable consequences; whereas in fact every single word in it was enough to have him burnt.

The only reply I will make to my sweetheart[2] is to send her a letter from Monsieur Dubucq, which I received at almost the same moment as hers.

I greet all three of you and embrace you with all my heart. Come on, give me your cheeks, my sweetheart; you, mother, let me have your hand; as for Mademoiselle Volland, she may give me anything.

Oh! I nearly forgot to tell you that I at last plucked up the courage to go and dine with Monsieur de Salverte[3] in the country. We had a very good day, quiet and simple. The young couple are in love and on the best of terms with their parents. On the

[1] *Le Vrai Système* by Dom Deschamps.
[2] Madame de Blacy.
[3] A rich financier.

way there, I stopped at the Casanoves'[1] and found Madame Casanove with still the same beautiful cheeks, beautiful eyes, and very beautiful teeth, as I made sure of telling her. Her husband was tolerant enough to look the other way from time to time, so that we could kiss without feeling embarrassed. Don't forget that all this was in the country and consequently quite without consequence.

## 39

*Paris, early September 1769*

No, my dear, no, you had no cause for complaint. I had already written to you, and at this very moment you will be getting another of my letters, for I don't believe any of those stories of letters going astray. And how could I forget that the 25th is your name-day? Knowing how interested you are in anything that concerns me, how could I fail to tell you about my success? Who else do you expect me to write to about it? Although there is hardly anyone in Paris, the theatre was full until the very last performance, and anyone who wanted to get in had to set about it well in advance. The actors were forced to give in to the demands of the pit and put it on twice more than they had intended. It was Monsieur Digeon who told me this last detail, which I knew nothing about—and indeed I swear to you that my friends have been more pleased by all this than I have myself. It is a long time since I made up my mind about the value of public applause, but now I have seen by experience that I was not deceiving myself in thinking I set little store by it. On Friday evening, at the last performance but one, Madame Diderot finally made up her mind to go with her daughter; she realized how unseemly it was to reply that she had not seen it when people complimented her on it. The actors surpassed themselves that day and in spite of herself she could not help being moved by the work and the performance. Her daughter told me that she was as deeply affected as any of the spectators.

What I liked best about all this was being kissed in a very

[1] François Casanove was the brother of the famous Casanova; his wife had been a dancer.

affectionate way by all the actresses, three or four of whom are not too shop-soiled.

How perversely things turn out in this world! Of all those whom I would have liked to have here and who would have been overjoyed at my success, one is no longer with us, another is roaming through Europe, and you are in the country. They say that all this should encourage me to write something else in this vein, but they don't know what they are talking about. I no longer have my old fire. You can take my word for it, the poet who stops writing has his reasons; whatever pretext he may give, the real cause of his idleness is that his inspiration has abandoned him. It is like an old person losing interest in racing about the place—if mama stills enjoys running around in spite of her sore foot, that means she is not old yet.

Since I take such pleasure in reading other people's writing, I suppose my own writing days are over. But we shall see: I have a certain *Sheriff*[1] running through my mind, and I really must get rid of him and of all the busybodies who keep asking after him. In the meantime, I am up to my eyes in work; I have been spending three or four days on end confined to my dressing-gown. Grimm will find his shop well stocked when he comes home. I have started on two or three books which were given to me ages ago by their poor long-suffering authors.

If I go to Le Grandval, I shall not come back before putting the finishing touch to my correspondence with Falconet. At the moment I am busy revising Abbé Galiani's book[2] and correcting the proofs. I don't know who will look after it when I am away. There is indeed a man who would be glad to do so, but I doubt if he would be up to it. All this is rather upsetting: I want to please the Baron, but I do not want to let the Abbé down, particularly when he is not here; I should not like him to think that out of sight is out of mind.

Here is another affair: Voltaire has sent me a comedy to present to the actors. Between ourselves, he has turned a splendid subject into a very mediocre sort of play. It is about Gourville entrusting half his fortune to a pious individual, who

[1] The plan of this rather melodramatic work has survived, but the play was never written.

[2] The *Dialogues sur le commerce des blés*, an attack on the economic theories of the Physiocrats.

subsequently denies having received anything, and half to Ninon, who returns every penny of it even though she has been quite destitute during Gourville's absence. Interspersed with this there are three or four grotesque comic characters. The play is in five acts and in verse. I doubt if the actors will take it, and even if they do, I doubt if the police will allow it; it is a dreadfully feeble copy of *Tartuffe*.[1]

Then there is yet another affair, and upon my word I don't know how we shall solve this one. The censor whom Sartine gave us for the Abbé's book is an out-and-out Capuchin who has been laying about him in all directions. I have already written four of five letters to the noble magistrate protesting on my honour that the man who has made the gaps should be kind enough to fill them up.

The only pleasures left to me are secretly writing a few lines to you and, when my head is exhausted, going next door to tease the mother and child. Yesterday the child was just about to go out and we had a little conversation which went something like this: 'What's that you have on your head that makes it look as big as a pumpkin?' 'It is a calash.'[2] 'But you are quite invisible inside your calash, if that's what it is.' 'All the better; it makes people look harder.' 'And do you like being looked at?' 'I don't dislike it.' 'You are a coquette then?' 'Perhaps. One person says: She is not bad, another one says: She is good-looking, and a third one says: She is pretty. You bring all these little compliments home with you and they give you pleasure.' 'Fine sort of pleasure!' 'Listen, papa, if I had to choose, I would prefer being admired a little by a lot of people to being admired a lot by just one. I have seen some of those great passions. They are terribly wearing if you don't share them, and it's even worse if you do.' 'Be off with you and take your calash with you.' 'Come now, leave us alone; we know quite well what suits us and the calash has its advantages, believe me.' 'What are they then?' 'In the first place, you can look out on the sly (that was her expression); then the top half of your face is in the shadow and that makes the bottom half look all the whiter, and then the size of the thing makes your face look dainty, etcetera.'

I think I told you that I had written a dialogue between

[1] Voltaire's comedy was *Le Dépositaire*; it was not performed in Paris.
[2] 'A woman's hood, supported with hoops, and projecting beyond the face' (*S.E.D.*).

d'Alembert and me. On reading it over, I had a fancy to write a sequel and did so. The speakers are d'Alembert dreaming, Bordeu, and d'Alembert's friend, Madmoiselle d'Espinasse. I have called it *D'Alembert's Dream*. You can't imagine anything more profound and more crazy. As an afterthought I added five or six pages which would make my sweetheart's hair stand on end, so she shall never set eyes on them. But the thing that will surprise you is that there is not a single word about religion and not a single indecent word in the whole piece. So I defy you to guess what it is about.

Talking of my sweetheart, I have sent her a letter from Monsieur Dubucq which should set her mind somewhat at rest. Tell her that I have done all she asked me and that I love her no less for all her scolding: lovers who do not quarrel from time to time are not really in love. I have not seen Madame Bouchard since I did her the small favour of sending her to the theatre. So she will kiss me on the street if she meets me there, will she! She is very welcome, wherever she likes; it is hard to be cruel towards women like her.

My Bordeaux actress[1] would drive me mad, if I did not have a certain interest in her wellbeing. Just think, she comes from a Protestant family and receives a pension of two hundred francs as a recent convert. Well, this recent convert, who is given two hundred francs a year for getting down on her knees when God is going by, took it into her head to make mock of His procession one day; her words were reported to the public prosecutor, a warrant was made for her arrest, and she was put in gaol, and only got out by paying.

Friend Perronet is very seriously ill; he is confined to his room and cannot talk to anybody. Poor Morellet is hard at work day and night composing a reply to Monsieur Necker.

I was invited to dinner at Châtillon today by Monsieur and Madame de Trudaine,[2] who have really taken a liking to me. I made my excuses as best I could, but in future I intend to take them up on it.

That play of mine has made quite a stir. I can just imagine how someone else might have taken advantage of it to get on

[1] Mademoiselle Jodin, whom Diderot helped and advised in her career.

[2] Jean-Charles Trudaine de Montigny occupied a high position in the Finance Department.

good terms with the whole of society. I shan't do that, unless I become a changed man. Even so, I could not avoid the blandishments and invitations of Monsieur and Madame de Salverte. I have already made two trips to their country house, which is one of the pleasantest places round Paris. It is as well-situated as Father La Chaise's house;[1] Paris seems to have been built for its sake.

Goodnight, my dears; continue loving me, unworthy as I am. Keep well; may Gras recover and these cursed rains not make you downcast. I have written to my sister to send me some wine; she will hardly have enough for her own needs, and if this weather lasts if will be expensive and undrinkable. But let us wait and see what the grape-harvest brings.

## 40

*Paris, 22 September 1769*

*The day after St. Matthew's day*

Yes indeed! you guessed quite right, my dear! He wrote to me from Berlin the day before the last performance to say that he had only another five or six hundred leagues to go. But at this last performance there was a very strange incident, which nearly spoiled the whole evening. At the moment where a noise is heard inside the house and Saint-Albin threatens to kill the first man who dares to lay hands on his mistress, a young woman in the front row cried out as piercingly as Saint-Albin and was taken ill.

This young woman was making her first appearance at the theatre after her marriage, as is the custom. The mishap brought me a visit from her husband, who climbed up to my fourth floor to thank me for the pleasure and pain I had given them. The husband is advocate general at the Bordeaux Courts; his name is Monsieur du Paty. We had a very pleasant chat. When he was leaving and had got as far as the landing, he modestly pulled a printed work out of his pocket and asked me to cast an indulgent eye over it, apologizing for his youthfulness and lack of talent.

[2] Père La Chaise was Louis XIV's Jesuit confessor. His country property later became the famous Père-Lachaise cemetery.

So off he went, and I started to read it and to my great surprise found myself reading a piece of writing full of eloquence, courage, and sound reasoning; it was a plea in favour of a woman who had been convicted of enjoying herself a little in her first year of widowhood and was thus, according to the law, in danger of losing all the advantages of her marriage contract. I have since learned that this same youthful magistrate denounced the vexations of the Duke of Richelieu, was bold enough to impose limits on the power of the governor and the law, and released from gaol several citizens who had been arbitrarily imprisoned. I have also learned that after humbling the provincial governor, he turned on the bishops who had annulled the marriages of Protestants and had forty of them rehabilitated. If the spirit of philosophy and patriotism could take hold of all those venerable heads, how marvellous that would be! It would not be easy, but it is not impossible. When I saw Monsieur du Paty again, I told him that on reading his speech I could only find consolation for my wounded vanity in the hope that with a wife and children he would fall a victim to the desire for comfort, peace, honour, and riches and all his talent would come to nothing. You would have smiled to see how naïvely he swore never to allow that to happen.

I must keep the tedious shop for at least eight or ten more days. I imagine that since the time when you were congratulating yourselves on the return of the fine weather, if the waters of the Marne have swollen anything like those of the Seine, the muddy river will be covering the *vordes* and besieging your castle. It is many years since comets were stripped of any influence over our affairs, but I cannot say for the life of me whether this was wise. You may say for your part that they make you lose at cards, but mama will say they make her win, and the result will be like everything else in the world, where one man's loss is another's gain.

Villichy or rather Villic[1] was a Prussian doctor who published several books, including the one you mention, in which he dealt with the miraculous properties of succinite and other natural substances. He did not die in Frankfurt, as President de Thou says, but in Lebus. If you want to know more about him and there is anyone in your region who needs any other philtre than

[1] Jodocus Willich, a sixteenth-century humanist and doctor.

a glass of good wine administered by you with a certain look in your eyes, I will borrow the book.

Are your crops still not in then? And the weevils are saving you the trouble of harvesting your turnips? That's what comes of not having them excommunicated.

The bridge at Neuilly is very fine; but the architect is still cooped up by his illness. Monsieur and Madame de Trudaine have developed a passion for me; if I had wanted to, I could have gone to two or three select dinner parties at Châtillon. I didn't, because I am an old bear, but I promised I would and that costs me nothing, because I never commit myself to keeping my promises. I cannot tell you anything about Monsieur or Madame Bouchard, as I have not seen either of them. I am as solitary as an anchorite. I would not dream of sending you my dialogues; that would be robbing myself of the pleasure of reading them to you. And then I think, without casting aspersions on your perspicacity, that they need a few words of commentary. The friend who was with me when I had dinner with the two monks is a man called Touche, whom you may have heard of through Madame Le Gendre, who knew him and thought highly of him. Your cheeks and your eyes, you say! You'd better go further than that or you'll be outdone by Madame Casanove. Here is the latest news, which will make you happy: Prince Golitsyn has just been made ambassador to the Hague; this is the best embassy there is and the least demanding. So now there he is, rich and idle for the rest of his life, settled at the centre of the world of painting and close to his friends; I am sure he is hugging himself for joy. He is leaving Saint Petersburg with his wife, who will have her baby in Berlin, and from there they will proceed to Holland.

I swear that I can see no more than what you see in the letter: a man who is taking advantage of a trifle which happened to please you in order to press his suit and using the opportunity of having to justify in your eyes the tender feelings which he formed without any encouragement from you and which he nevertheless hoped he might make you share. It is quite a clever plan. Whether he succeeded or not, he would have had his say. But he hardly knows you; you do not need to answer him.

Goodnight, dear ladies. I am worn to a shred and it is high time Grimm took over his shop again.

41

*Paris, 12 October 1770*

My dear ladies,

Well then, let me tell you about my bad behaviour. Let me go back to the Friday morning when I was carried off from Isle at ten or eleven o'clock.[1] We got to Châlons at six in the evening. Madame Duclos heard the sound of horses and a carriage coming into her street; she ran to her door, thinking she was going to embrace Madame de Maux and Madame de Prunevaux, whom she was expecting that day; just imagine her surprise when she saw me, whom she hadn't been expecting at all. But she gave me a warm welcome for all that.

I had thought that Madame de Maux was still detained at Bourbonne by some feminine ailment. She had written to me at Langres that Doctor Juvet had condemned her to stay there until the twenty-fifth. So I was travelling without knowing where she was and she without knowing where I was, but we could not have timed it better if we had planned it all in advance.

At seven o'clock, one hour after me, along came another postilion, more horses and more carriages. It was Madame de Maux, Madame de Prunevaux, and a certain Monsieur de Foissy,[2] equerry to the Duke of Chartres, a man of thirty, but with the sense and judgement of a man of forty-five, extremely thoughtful, kind, polite, simple, and cheerful. In serving the great he had acquired the sciatica which had taken him to Bourbonne. There he had met the ladies. He had grown very attached to them, and they to him. He had put off his return so as to be able to go with them. He had let one of the chambermaids have his post-chaise and had taken the vacant seat in Madame de Maux's carriage. They had taken him to Vandœuvre to see Monsieur de Provenchères with whom he was not previously acquainted and who gave him the sort of welcome he deserved. And now he was arriving with them at Châlons to see Madame

[1] Diderot was on his way back to Paris from the spa of Bourbonne, not far from Langres, where he had been with Madame de Maux—with whom he was having his last love-affair—and her daughter Madame de Prunevaux. The Madame Duclos whom they all visit is the same lady whom we saw with Madame de Maux by the dying Damilaville's bedside in 1768.

[2] At this period he was supplanting Diderot in Madame de Maux's affections.

Duclos, with whom he had likewise not been previously acquainted and who gave him a good welcome for all that.

So there we were all together at Châlons in Duclos's house, and his wife in raptures to have us there. I have never seen a happier person in all my life; she did everything she possibly could to make our stay agreeable, and with a genuine show of feeling which I cannot convey to you. You should have seen it. I spent the Saturday and the Sunday at Châlons. I left there on the Monday morning. Madame de Maux and the others stayed two days longer.

On the Sunday it was the end of the theatre season. We went to see the play. The actor who was making a speech to the audience knew I was there and treated me in public to a compliment which was not too badly turned. You know what I am like. Imagine how embarrassed I was. I hid myself lower and lower in the box and in my modesty nearly lost myself in the ladies' petticoats.

The house was still sleeping, except for the lady of the house, when our horses were put to, and we had breakfast and took our leave. Good Madame Duclos was all in tears, and so was her husband. I was weeping too and my little son-in-law[1] had gone out to prevent himself from succumbing. I was told that there was the same sorrowful scene when they parted from Madame de Maux. I arrived here at nightfall on the twenty-sixth of September. I would have arrived in time for dinner if our little postilion had not taken the Soissons road instead of the Paris road as we were leaving Château-Thierry. We left Château-Thierry at half past eight in the morning and thanks to this mistake, we had to retrace our steps, and were back in Château-Thierry at four in the afternoon.

I am never lacking in little day-to-day worries; just think how many of them I found waiting for me after two months' absence. My wife was well; my daughter had been ill, really very ill, and was still not well. She is getting better now. For my part, I have already lost all the healthy vigour and gaiety I acquired on my travels. The first three days I was back here I felt as if I were living in a poisoned atmosphere. I have been so busy bustling about that I have made myself ill. I was unable

[1] Caroillon de Vandeul had become engaged to Diderot's daughter in March 1770. The couple married in 1772.

to go out for three days. It passed, but three days later it started again; my stomach is in a bad way and my intestines are not doing their job properly. Then it was my name-day and to keep everyone happy I had to take part in a little orgy, and that finished me off.

As soon as I got back, I went to see Monsieur and Madame Digeon.[1] Only Madame was at home, with mourning clothes and a happy, healthy face. We chatted for about two hours. Yesterday I met Monsieur Digeon. We embraced very lovingly. I told him how highly you and I thought of him.

A few days earlier I had been to call on Madame Bouchard. I spent a very gay evening there. She and I and Abbé I-forget-his-name de la Chaux philosophized together very soundly and very extravagantly. I thought she was looking well. We have made an agreement about butterflies, if there are any. For every butterfly there will be a kiss, but never two kisses in the same place, and as there will be a lot of butterflies, I hope that there will not be an inch of my person which will not be kissed several times over; unless, that is, the lady prefers to exchange all those kisses for a single one which I will give her on a place to be chosen by me.

I have been to La Briche, where Monsieur Grimm and Madame d'Épinay have taken refuge from the masons who are demolishing the gable of the house which Madame d'Épinay occupies, or occupied, in the Rue Sainte-Anne. By dint of hard work I have caught up with my affairs; before long my health and happiness will return. When? When you return. I hope and give everyone else to hope that this will be very soon, and it is such a pleasant thought that they all let themselves be convinced without difficulty.

I embrace you all with all my heart. I begin with mama. Do not accuse me, or her either, of forgetting my birthday. On that very same day when she was celebrating her name-day, a pretty child was being started on his way who will love her, respect her and remain attached to her all his life.[2] After mama, by rights, it is my sweetheart's turn. If I felt so inclined, I would not say a single loving word to her, because she knows me and can

[1] Mademoiselle Élisabeth Le Gendre had married the tutor Digeon after her mother's death.

[2] Madame Diderot's name-day was on 4 October, Diderot's birthday on the 5th.

rely on me and will never be led by distance, silence, and absence to doubt my feelings for her. As for you, Mademoiselle Volland, think what is owing to you; I need say no more. And then, addressing all three at once, I repeat what I have so often sworn to you, that more than ever you are infinitely dear to me, that my feelings can never change, that I have resolved—no, it is not a resolution, it is a very genuine, very ancient, unvarying inclination which impels me to you, and which I am neither able nor anxious to resist. Come back to Paris, come and you will find in me perhaps not the man you expect to find, but the man I have always been.

Goodbye, my dear loving friends. Goodbye.

42

*Paris, 28 November 1770*

My dear, I begged you not to let a post go by without giving me news of mama, and you have not written a word.[1] It is this silence that is really cruel. I do not even know if you have had Bordeu's opinion, which I went for straight away and put in the post the following day. If I had been guilty of this crime, Heaven knows how I should have been treated.

I take my wishes for facts, and assume that all is well. I cannot believe that your fears are still with you and you are hiding them from me. Am I no longer worthy of sharing your troubles? My dear good friends, this is no moment to choose for growing cool, believe me. Never have I stood in greater need of someone to love me and be loved by me. I have been relying on you for the rest of my life; if you abandon me, I shall be left alone.

My daughter's health is deteriorating from day to day. She doesn't tell me so, because she is afraid of distressing me, but I can see it for myself. This casts a shadow over my whole day. Since almost her only pleasure is to have me with her, I go out very little. When I was in the provinces and in the country I acquired a taste for solitude which makes me shun company. I live here in my study, working, dreaming and writing, not

[1] Madame Volland lived until 1772.

happy, but happier than I should be elsewhere it seems, since I hate having to take off my dressing-gown.

Tell me that you love me and that you have faith in my undying affection for you. And tell me too that mama is drinking, eating and sleeping, and that she is well again, and you will have given me some very happy moments.

43

*The Hague, 18 June 1773*

Good friends, I arrived on Tuesday morning at The Hague. I could have been here by the Monday evening, but it was late and I was too tired. I kept in good health on the way. I am feeling very well now. The prince[1] has given me the sort of welcome I expected. The princess is absent, she has gone to see her family in Berlin, and the prince swears that if I left his house before making her acquaintance he would have a divorce on his hands. We live a bachelor life together. I have an agreeable apartment and they have taken on an extra servant for me alone.

I crossed the river at Moerdijk, an expanse of water which gives some idea of the sea. On my first day here I went to pay my respects to Neptune and his vast empire, which is only half a league away. Yesterday I visited the schools at Leyden. I have seen paintings, engravings, princes, and scholars. We have all sorts of wild plans. If we manage to execute them, I shall see a lot and not go short of entertainment. I shall not be much at home, and I shall do almost no work. Yet I should very much like to work.

I am only writing a few words to you. In future too I shall be laconic with you. I shall save everything up for the sweet moments which we still have to spend together. I greet you both and embrace you lovingly. As long as I live I shall keep my first feelings for you, Mademoiselle Volland. Take care of yourself, I beg you, my dear. We shall meet again, and perhaps before very long.

Please give my regards to Monsieur and Madame Bouchard, to Monsieur and Madame Digeon, and to Monsieur Gaschon

[1] Prince Golitsyn.

when you see him. If you can persuade Monsieur Duval to help my children with their plans, I hope you will not fail to do so. Whatever he does, I shall keep the same attachment and regard for him. Do not miss me as much as I miss you; you would be too unhappy. True friendship does not diminish with distance, and my heart touches yours as if we were sitting by the same fireside. Goodbye to you both. I repeat to you my oath of eternal and inviolable love.

## 44

*The Hague, 22 July 1773*

My dear ladies,

The more I see of this country, the more I like it. The soles, fresh herring, turbots and perch, and all the things they call 'water-fish' are excellent company. The walks are delightful; I don't know if the women are very virtuous, but with their great straw hats, their downcast eyes, and the huge scarves they wear on their chests, they all look as if they had just got back from church or were on their way to confession. The men are sensible; they understand their affairs very well; they are thoroughly imbued with republican spirit, from the highest to the lowest in the land. I heard a saddler say: 'I must get my daughter out of that convent quickly. I am afraid she may pick up some royalist servility there.' This was about a daughter he was having educated in Brussels.

I shan't say much about the country; I want to have something to tell you about when I am relaxing by your fireside, when I have the pleasure of seeing you again; for I hope you will take care to look after yourselves both for your friends and for me—I have resolved to love you as long as you and I shall live, and for this reason and many others I hope to live a very long time.

The princess has returned from her travels. She is a very lively, gay, and witty woman and quite nice-looking—better than 'quite'—young, educated and full of accomplishments. She is well-read; she knows several languages, as German women often do. She plays the harpsichord and sings quite angelically.

She is full of naïve and droll remarks. She is very kind. She said at table yesterday that to meet a poor man gave her such pleasure that she willingly forgave Providence for putting a few of them on to the streets. We had a blockhead here who was regretting not having had his portrait painted in Paris; she asked him if he was there when Oudry[1] was still working. She is extremely sensitive, rather too much so for her own happiness. Being both knowledgeable and intelligent, she argues like a young lion. I am mad about her and live with the prince and his wife as I might with a good brother and a good sister.

This is the place for spending your days profitably. No one wastes your time by calling for you every morning. The trouble is that we go to bed very late and get up late too. We lead a quiet, abstemious, secluded life.

I have met two old men here who were extremely influential in government affairs until recently; now they are no longer at the centre of things and quite rightly they do not like this retirement. What with their solemn manner and their serious, austere way of speaking, I really felt as if I were with a Fabius and a Regulus. There is no one so like the ancient Romans as these two venerable characters. They are the two Bentincks, Charles Bentinck and Bentinck van Rhoon.

I have written two or three rather entertaining little pieces. I hardly ever go out; when I do, I always go by the sea, which I have not yet seen either calm or rough. The vast monotonous expanse and the murmuring noise make you dream; I have good dreams there.

I have looked unsuccessfully for various books. The foreigners have snapped up all I was hoping to find.

I am beginning to feel my Achilles' heel, which is, as you know, my stomach. For the first month I thought I was cured.

I greet you and embrace you with all my heart. My compliments and regards to Monsieur and Madame Bouchard; to Monsieur and Madame Digeon; to Monsieur Duval, to whom I owe a debt of gratitude for the interest which he takes in your affairs and which he was kind enough to take in mine.

Remember me to Monsieur Gaschon when you see him.

I hope your domestic troubles are soon successfully sorted out.

[1] Jean-Baptiste Oudry, an animal painter who died in 1755.

I am united with you for as long as I live; wherever the gods take me, I shall take you in my heart.

## 45

*Saint Petersburg, 29 December 1773*

My dear friend,

After a fortnight's torture caused by the waters of the Neva, I have rallied round and am in good health again. I am still as much in favour with Her Imperial Majesty as before. I shall have made the most splendid voyage imaginable by the time I get home. Grimm and I will be leaving some time in February. I greet you and embrace you as lovingly as ever. A thousand tender compliments to Madame de Blacy my sweetheart and to Monsieur and Madame Bouchard, Abbé Le Monnier and Monsieur Gaschon. What a lot we shall have to say to one another by your fireside!

It is New Year's Eve. What more need I say!

## 46

*The Hague, 9 April 1774*

My dear ladies,

After travelling 700 leagues in 22 days, I arrived in The Hague on the 5th of this month, in excellent health and less tired from my immense journey than I have often been from a short walk. I am returning to you heaped with honours. If I had wanted to help myself from the imperial treasury, I think I should have been perfectly free to do so; but I preferred to stop the mouths of the envious in Saint Petersburg and win the belief of the incredulous in Paris. All the ideas which filled my head on leaving Paris vanished during my first night in Saint Petersburg. In this way I was able to behave more honestly and disinterestedly. Since I had nothing to hope or fear, I could say what I pleased.

When shall we have the happiness of seeing one another

again? Perhaps in a fortnight, perhaps much later. The Empress has given me the job of publishing the regulations of the many useful institutions which she has created.[1] If the Dutch publisher is as extortionate as usual, I shall have no more to do with him and shall go and publish in Paris. If I can get reasonable terms, I shall stay here until the job is done; it won't last for ever.

Although the weather was as fine as if we had ordered it specially, and we had excellent travelling on very good roads, that didn't stop us breaking up four carriages on our way home. When I recall crossing the Dvina at Riga on broken ice floes, which spurted out water all round us, rising and sinking under the weight of our carriage and cracking on every side, I still shudder at the thought of the danger we were in. I nearly broke an arm and a shoulder on a ferry at Mittau; there were thirty men carrying our post-chaise, in constant danger of falling and shooting us all pell-mell into the river. At Hamburg we were forced to send our trunks to Amsterdam by post-cart. A post-chaise carrying any weight would never have coped with the difficult roads.

I am staying with Prince Golitsyn, whose joy on seeing me again you can imagine if you think of the pleasure you will feel before very long.

I think I have already told you that after receiving me in the kindest possible way and allowing me to come into her cabinet every day between three and five or six o'clock, the Empress was good enough to agree to all the requests I made on taking my leave. I asked her to meet the cost of my journey there, my stay and my return home, reminding her that a philosopher does not travel in the same style as a great lord. She granted me that. I asked her to give me a trifle whose only value would be in the fact that she had used it, and she granted me that, very graciously and with all the marks of the highest esteem. I shall tell you all about it, if I haven't already done so. I asked her for one of her court officers to bring me back safe and sound where I wanted to be, and she granted me that and personally ordered my carriage and the preparations for the journey.

My dear ladies, I swear that this period in my life has been as gratifying as one could imagine for my self-esteem. And I tell

[1] General Betzky's *Plans et statuts des différents établissements ordonnés par l'Impératrice Catherine II* was published in Amsterdam in 1775.

you, you will have to believe what I say about that extraordinary woman, for my praises will be unpaid and will not come from venal lips.

I greet you, embrace you, and send you my most loving respect. You are very unjust if you do not believe that I have come back with the same feelings I had on leaving you; if anything is changed, it is not my heart, but your minds.

My regards to Madame Bouchard. If you see Monsieur Gaschon, remember me to him. Mademoiselle Volland, I embrace you with all my heart. But are you still not better?

## 47

*The Hague, 3 September 1774*

My dear ladies,

My boxes were sent off to Rotterdam yesterday; all the treasure I have left is what will fit into a travelling bag for five or six days.

Prince and Princess Golitsyn are doing their utmost to keep me here until the end of the month. According to them I should wait here until they receive the final decision of the Russian court concerning a project which the Empress herself has declared must be executed this month, but I shall do nothing of the kind. The publication of her book is not finished yet, but I have determined to give the printer one more week; when that time is up I shall leave the job to anyone who will take it.

In spite of all my hosts' kindness and the charms of Holland, I am dying with impatience; I need to see you all again. If anyone had told me when I left Paris, as I thought, for a voyage of five or six months, that I would be away nearly three times as long, I would have called him a liar. But now at last I am returning home for good. The time has gone when I could count by years, now I must count by days. The smaller your revenue, the more important it is to spend it well. I may have another ten years to go. I shall lose two or three of the ten to chills, rheumatisms, and all the rest of that tedious family; I must try to keep the other seven for a quiet life and such little pleasures as life can still afford after the age of sixty. Such is my intention, and I hope you will support me in it.

I used to think that the fibres of the heart hardened with age; not a bit of it. I am not sure that I am not more impressionable than before; everything touches me, everything moves me; I shall be the biggest old crybaby you have ever seen.

Goodbye, dear ladies; in just a short time now we shall meet again. I greet you and embrace you with all my heart. Madame de Blacy, I am told that during my absence someone has been cutting the ground from under my feet. If you are still the woman you were, you would have done just as well to keep me. If you have abandoned your strict principles I congratulate you on your wickedness and inconstancy. How Madame Bouchard will kiss me if she still has the same taste for natural history! I have brought back pieces of marble and each of them will be worth a kiss, and metals and each of them will be worth a kiss, and minerals and each of them will be worth a kiss. How will she ever pay for the whole of Siberia? If every kiss is to be in a different place, I advise her to get together some friends to accept some of the kisses on her behalf. Of course my kisses will be as small as I can make them, but Siberia is very large.

You would have been as bad as me if you had allowed me to forget Monsieur and Madame Digeon. Give Monsieur Gaschon my greetings if you see him before me. I imagine he has not yet resigned his office as the satellite of Pleasure, the most irregular of all the planets, which carries him to the remotest horizons. Goodbye, dear friends. Goodbye; soon I shall reappear on your horizon, and never leave it.

# INDEX

Douane
Augustins
PLACE DES VICTOIRE
R. des Bons Enfans
LA BOURSE
Rue Colbert